SEPTEMBER 2021–AUGUST 2022

TABLE OF CONTENTS

PRECEPTS FOR LIVING® PERSONAL STUDY GUIDE

SEPTEMBER 2021–AUGUST 2022

TABLE OF CONTENTS

PRECEPTS FOR LIVING® PERSONAL STUDY GUIDE

INTRODUCTION

Welcome to the *Precepts For Living®* Personal Study Guide! While using it, we hope that you will find it to be an enlightening and rewarding experience. This study guide can be used as a reference tool for any teacher or student who is serious about learning and knowing the inspired Word of God. It is designed to be used in conjunction with the *Precepts For Living®* Annual Commentary. It should help you get the God-intended meaning of each Scripture presented and explained in the commentary. Therefore, it is suggested that you use the guide in the following way:

- Thoroughly study each lesson in the *Precepts For Living®* Annual Commentary. Go to the companion lesson in this study guide and answer all the questions pertaining to the lesson.
- After you have answered all the questions for a particular lesson on your own, check your answers by using the answer key, which is found in the back of this book.
- If you miss an answer, go back and research it in the *Precepts For Living®* Annual Commentary. This will enhance both your learning experience and memorization of Scripture.

Enjoy this *Precepts For Living®* Personal Study Guide. As you do your Bible study, observe Scripture, grasp it by correctly interpreting the text, and then walk in the knowledge of God's Word.

Precepts For Living® Personal Study Guide was written and prepared by Judith St. Clair Hull, PhD.

"Who is like unto thee, O LORD, among the gods? who is like thee, glorious in holiness, fearful in praises, doing wonders?" (Exodus 15:11, KJV)

SEPTEMBER 5, 2021

MOSES AND MIRIAM PRAISE GOD

EXODUS 15:11–21

Use with Bible Study Guide 1.

WORDS, PHRASES, AND DEFINITIONS

Write the definition of the following words.

1. Redeemed: ______________________________
2. Habitation: ______________________________
3. Anguish: ______________________________
4. Sanctuary: ______________________________
5. Timbrel: ______________________________
6. Genocide: ______________________________
7. Annihilation: ______________________________
8. Inhabitants: ______________________________
9. Surpassed: ______________________________
10. Holiness: ______________________________

JUMP-STARTING THE LESSON

11. Unscramble the word. (In Focus)

    Ramona prayed to God that He would bring her to (F E T A S Y) ______________________ .

12. Ramona used these words to thank God. "P______________ God. God is

    g______________."

UNDERSTANDING THE LESSON

13. Look at verse 19 and see what happened to Pharaoh, his chariots, and his horsemen. (Focal Verses)

   a. They went into the ____________________.

   b. The Lord brought the ____________________ upon them.

14. Write TRUE or FALSE concerning Miriam. (The People, Places, and Times)

   a. ____________________ She was the younger sister of Moses.

   b. ____________________ She watched over her baby brother.

   c. ____________________ She got her mother to help care for Moses.

   d. ____________________ She led the people in praise and worship dance.

15. Draw lines to the right number to put the events of the Israelite history in order. (Background)

a. They lived freely in Goshen.	1
b. Jacob and his family moved to Egypt.	2
c. God freed them through mighty miracles.	3
d. A new pharaoh enslaved them.	4

16. Moses, Miriam, and the people sang to (R A E P I S) ____________________ God. (In Depth)

17. They sang to be (E A R D H) ____________________.

18. They sang to (M E M R E B E R) ____________________.

COMMITTING TO THE WORD

19. Memorize and write verbatim:

   Exodus 15:11 ____

   ____

   ____

WALKING IN THE WORD

20. Choose a song to praise the Lord that you can sing all week.

   ____

   ____

   ____

"And David and all the house of Israel played before the LORD on all manner of instruments made of fir wood, even on harps, and on psalteries, and on timbrels, and on cornets, and on cymbals." (2 Samuel 6:5, KJV)

SEPTEMBER 12, 2021

DAVID DANCES BEFORE THE ARK

2 SAMUEL 6:1–5, 14–19

Use with Bible Study Guide 2.

WORDS, PHRASES, AND DEFINITIONS

Write the definition of the following words.

1. Cherubim: ______________________________
2. Psaltery: ______________________________
3. Lyre: ______________________________
4. Cornet: ______________________________
5. Castanet: ______________________________
6. Ephod: ______________________________
7. Tabernacle: ______________________________
8. Flagon: ______________________________
9. Extraction: ______________________________
10. Deterred: ______________________________

JUMP-STARTING THE LESSON

11. New musicians in Pastor Michael's church wanted to change to a more contemporary (Y L S T E) ____________________ of music. (In Focus)

12. Pastor Michael escaped to his study and (A Y E D P R) ____________________.

UNDERSTANDING THE LESSON

13. Name the five instruments listed in verse 5. (Focal Verses)

KJV	NLT
1.____________________	1. ____________________
2. ____________________	2. ____________________

3. ____________________ 3. ____________________

4. ____________________ 4. ____________________

5. ____________________ 5. ____________________

14. Put the locations of the Ark in numerical order. (The People, Places, and Times)

_______ With the Philistines

_______ In the Tabernacle in the wilderness

_______ Beth-shemesh

_______ In the Tabernacle in Bethel

_______ Kiriath-jearim

15. What was one of David's top priorities once he became king? (Background) ____________________

16. How did King David attempt to move the Ark the first time? (In Depth)

Upon a new cart | Pulled by horses | With a man holding each corner

17. How did David move the Ark the second time?

The same as the first time | On the shoulders of the Levite priests | Pushing the cart

18. Put the events from verses 14 through 19 in numerical order.

_______ Michal, Saul's daughter, despised King David.

_______ David offered burnt offerings.

_______ David danced before the Lord.

_______ David gave everyone gifts of bread, dates, and raisins.

COMMITTING TO THE WORD

19. Memorize and write verbatim:

2 Samuel 6:5 ____

____

WALKING IN THE WORD

20. This week look online for videos of praise dancing and share them with the class next week.

____

____

"And Jesus answered and said unto him, What wilt thou that I should do unto thee? The blind man said unto him, Lord, that I might receive my sight." (Mark 10:51, KJV)

GLORIFYING GOD

MARK 10:46–52

Use with Bible Study Guide 3.

WORDS, PHRASES, AND DEFINITIONS

Write the definition of the following words.

1. Mercy: ______________________________
2. Jewish heritage: ______________________________
3. Royal lineage: ______________________________
4. Metaphor: ______________________________
5. Exercise his faith: ______________________________
6. Hindrance: ______________________________
7. Religious obligation: ______________________________
8. Marginalized by society: ______________________________
9. Narrative: ______________________________
10. Impending: ______________________________

JUMP-STARTING THE LESSON

11. What terrible event happened to the Johnsons just two months after moving into a new area? (In Focus)

    Hurricane — Tornado

    Divorce — Death in the family

12. Fill in the blanks to show what the Johnsons prayed for.

    A ____________________ for Herman

    An open ____________________ for Shelly so she could work as a beautician

UNDERSTANDING THE LESSON

13. What is the beginning scene of today's Scripture? Fill in the blanks: (Focal Verses)

Jesus of ____________________ was just outside of ____________________ when a man named ____________________ called out to him.

14. Underline the things that happened in Jericho. (The People, Places, and Times)

Joshua and his forces destroyed the city.

Zacchaeus lived in the city.

Jesus was born there.

15. Draw lines to show who called Jesus by what name.

Bartimaeus	Jesus of Nazareth
The crowd	Rabboni
	Son of David

16. What did Bartimaeus cry out to Jesus? (In Depth)

Jesus, Son of ____________________, have ____________________ on me.

17. Who said what? Write in the blanks: the crowd, Bartimaeus, Jesus.

____________________ Be quiet!

____________________ Son of David, have mercy on me!

____________________ Tell him to come here.

____________________ Cheer up, Come on, he's calling you!

18. What did Bartimaeus ask Jesus to do? Fill in the last word. "I want to ____________________."

COMMITTING TO THE WORD

19. Memorize and write verbatim:

Mark 10:51 ____

____

WALKING IN THE WORD

20. Look for someone in church today that others seem to ignore and write down ways you are making them feel welcome.

____

____

____

SEPTEMBER 26, 2021

"And they continued stedfastly in the apostles' doctrine and fellowship, and in breaking of bread, and in prayers."
(Acts 2:42, KJV)

BELIEVERS PRAISE GOD

ACTS 2:32–33, 37–47

Use with Bible Study Guide 4.

WORDS, PHRASES, AND DEFINITIONS

Write the definition of the following words.

1. Monsoons: ______________________________
2. Doctrine: ______________________________
3. Exalted: ______________________________
4. Untoward: ______________________________
5. Apostles: ______________________________
6. Had all things common: ______________________________
7. One accord: ______________________________
8. Firstfruits: ______________________________
9. Bestowal: ______________________________
10. Convicting: ______________________________

JUMP-STARTING THE LESSON

11. Jessica wanted a new church building to house a ____________________ kitchen and provide ____________________ for the homeless in the community. (In Focus)

12. Jessica came to understand that the community of faith is much larger than the four ____________________ of her local ____________________ body.

UNDERSTANDING THE LESSON

13. What were Peter and the other apostles witnesses of? (Focal Verses)

God ____________________ Jesus from the dead.

14. What was the other name the Old Testament gave to Pentecost? (The People, Places, and Times)

___________________ of ___________________.

15. What promise from Jesus were the apostles waiting for in the upper room? (Background) ______________

____

16. Draw arrows in the blanks to show that the Trinity is a community of love demonstrated in the giving of the Holy Spirit. (In Depth)

The Father the Son the Holy Spirit

17. The Holy Spirit is the birthright of every true ___________________-___________________

___________________ in Christ.

RNBO GINAA LEVBEIRE

18. Underline the sentences that were true of the first community of believers.

1. Everyone was willing to share all they had with the others.
2. They met daily in the Temple.
3. They met in homes for the Lord's Supper.
4. They shared with great joy and generosity.

COMMITTING TO THE WORD

19. Memorize and write verbatim:

Acts 2:42 ____

____

____

____

WALKING IN THE WORD

20. Think of some way to share Jesus with someone this week.

____

____

____

____

____

"Know ye that the LORD he is God: it is he that hath made us, and not we ourselves; we are his people, and the sheep of his pasture." (Psalm 100:3, KJV)

MAKE A JOYFUL NOISE

PSALM 100

Use with Bible Study Guide 5.

WORDS, PHRASES, AND DEFINITIONS

Write the definition of the following words.

1. Endureth: ______________________________
2. Commodity: ______________________________
3. Analogy: ______________________________
4. Zion: ______________________________
5. Pilgrimage: ______________________________
6. Enthrone Him: ______________________________
7. Gates: ______________________________
8. Liturgical psalm: ______________________________
9. Summons: ______________________________
10. Exhortation: ______________________________

JUMP-STARTING THE LESSON

11. What was Noah focusing on in the football field? (In Focus) First, he had to focus on his

____________________ and his ____________________.

C G R A H P Y H O R E O   S I T P O O I N G I N

12. Noah knew his parents would be ____________________ and ____________________.

G I N S I N G   E E C H R N I G

UNDERSTANDING THE LESSON

13. Draw lines between the phrases from the KJV and the NLT: (Focal Verses)

1. Make a joyful noise	a. His faithfulness
2. All ye lands	b. Shout with joy
3. Serve the LORD	c. Unfailing love
4. His mercy	d. Continues forever
5. Everlasting	e. All the earth
6. His truth	f. Worship the LORD

14. In what way is the Lord like our shepherd? (The People, Places, and Times)

He takes ____________________ of us.

15. Three times a year the Israelites made a pilgrimage to Jerusalem. What were the pilgrimages meant to remind the people of? (Background)

Jerusalem was their capital.

Walking is good exercise.

They were the people of God united by their worship of the one true God.

16. Whom was the psalm meant to summon? (In Depth)

All people   The Israelites   Good singers

17. Circle the words that show what God's people are urged to do.

Joyful noise   gladness   singing   thanksgiving   praise   thanks   bless

18. Check the reasons for worshiping the Lord.

_______ The Lord is good.

_______ His love is secure forever.

_______ He is faithful to us in spite of ourselves.

COMMITTING TO THE WORD

19. Memorize and write verbatim.

Psalm 100:3 ____

____

WALKING IN THE WORD

20. Write a psalm of praise for the Lord:

____

____

"And he shall judge the world in righteousness, he shall minister judgment to the people in uprightness." (Psalm 9:8, KJV)

OCTOBER 10, 2021

PRAISE GOD FOR JUSTICE AND RIGHTEOUSNESS

PSALM 9:1–12

Use with Bible Study Guide 6.

WORDS, PHRASES, AND DEFINITIONS

Write the definition of the following words.

1. Complacent: ____________________
2. Convened: ____________________
3. Cronies: ____________________
4. Galvanized: ____________________
5. Satest: ____________________
6. Inquisition: ____________________
7. Parallelism: ____________________
8. Superscription: ____________________
9. Corporate: ____________________
10. Laud: ____________________

JUMP-STARTING THE LESSON

11. Why were residents of Rucker Heights unable to remove an ineffective village board? (In Focus)

    No one was willing to ____________ ____________ ____________.

12. What was the slogan that Elder Timothy Shields used? We had to be the ____________ we wanted to see.

UNDERSTANDING THE LESSON

13. God is for justice. Who are some of those He judges in favor of? (Focal Verses)

The ____________________, the ____________________, and the ____________________.

PROSPESDE EPHLESLS UMHLEB

14. Write down the number of psalms each person/persons wrote: (The People, Places, and Times)

_____ David, _____ Asaph, _____ sons of Korah, _____ Solomon, _____ Heman, _____ Ethan, _____ Moses

15. Psalms 9 and 10 are thought to have been one psalm. Fill in the words of the theme: (Background)

God's ability to execute ____________________ and ____________________.

16. Look at the end of verse 4 in both translations and write down how God judges: (In Depth)

God judges ____________________ (KJV). God judges with ____________________ (NLT).

17. David worships God because He is the one qualified to decide what is

____________________ and ____________________.

IGRHT STJU

COMMITTING TO THE WORD

18. Memorize and write verbatim.

Psalm 9:8 ____

____

____

____

WALKING IN THE WORD

19. Write down a difficult situation from this week in which you are practicing God's justice.

____

____

____

____

“Then they cried unto the LORD in their trouble, and he delivered them out of their distresses.” (Psalm 107:6, KJV)

OCTOBER 17, 2021

GIVE THANKS FOR DELIVERANCE

PSALM 107:1-9, 39-43

Use with Bible Study Guide 7.

WORDS, PHRASES, AND DEFINITIONS

Write the definition of the following words.

1. Cardiac arrest: ____________________
2. Arterial blockage: ____________________
3. Stent: ____________________
4. Minished: ____________________
5. Whoso: ____________________
6. Levites: ____________________
7. Onerous: ____________________
8. Admonishing: ____________________
9. Exile: ____________________
10. Dispersed: ____________________

JUMP-STARTING THE LESSON

11. Circle the symptoms of cardiac arrest that Dorcas was experiencing. (In Focus)

    Weakness   Out of breath   Pain in the heart   Hurting back   Pain in the neck

12. When the doctors saw where the arterial blockage was, they put in a ____________________.

UNDERSTANDING THE LESSON

13. What people should give thanks to God? (Focal Verses) D E R E M E D E ____________________

14. Moses composed Psalm 90 around ____________________. Ethan composed Psalm 89 around ____________________. (The People, Places, and Times)

15. What did God redeem the Israelites from? (Background)

    Babylonian ____________________.

16. Why should people give thanks and praise the Lord? (In Depth)

    The Lord is ____________________.

    His steadfast ____________________ endures forever.

17. When did the Lord deliver His people?

    When they ____________________ unto the LORD in their trouble, He delivered them.

18. What does God want His people to rely upon? In the KJV, the word is the lovingkindness of the LORD. In the NLT lovingkindness is translated as two words: ____________________ ____________________.

COMMITTING TO THE WORD

19. Memorize and write verbatim.

    Psalm 107:6 ____________________

WALKING IN THE WORD

20. Make a special list of those who need God's deliverance that you can pray for this week.

"Blessed are they that dwell in thy house: they will be still praising thee. Selah." (Psalm 84:4, KJV)

OCTOBER 24, 2021

THE JOY OF WORSHIP

PSALM 84

Use with Bible Study Guide 8.

WORDS, PHRASES, AND DEFINITIONS

Write the definition of the following words.

1. Amiable: ____________________
2. Selah: ____________________
3. Lord of hosts: ____________________
4. Remnant: ____________________
5. Insatiable: ____________________
6. Catalyst: ____________________
7. Edifices: ____________________
8. Blessed: ____________________
9. Meditate: ____________________
10. Anointed: ____________________

JUMP-STARTING THE LESSON

11. Where all had Mardelle and Theodore called home? (In Focus)

    Africa   Central America   Europe   South America

12. Where did Mardelle live after Theodore died?

    Family home in South Carolina   Paris, France

UNDERSTANDING THE LESSON

13. Find "blessed" in the KJV. What two words does the NLT use to translate this? (Focal Verses)

____________________   ____________________

14. After the rebellion of Korah, many were destroyed, including Korah himself, but his sons were not killed. How did the sons of Korah respond? (The People, Places, and Times)

a. They avoided all things of the Lord.

b. They had a great attraction to the house of the Lord.

c. They wrote many psalms.

15. Underline the positions that the sons of Korah held: (Background)

Porters Musicians Living in God's house

16. How did the sons of Korah feel about being in the Temple in God's presence: (In Depth)

a. Fainting with longing to be in His presence

b. Shouting joyfully to the Lord

c. Always singing God's praises

d. Worried that they couldn't sing in tune

17. What does God do for those who go through the valley of tears?

They will find their ____________________ in the Lord.

18. When the psalmist goes through times of trouble, what does he ask God to do? ____________________

____________________ ____________________.

19. Any day in the presence of God is more precious than a ____________________ days anywhere else.

COMMITTING TO THE WORD

20. Memorize and write verbatim.

Psalm 84:4 ____

____

____

____

WALKING IN THE WORD

21. Think of a hymn that has always moved you. Write down what makes it special to your life.

____

____

____

____

"Let every thing that hath breath praise the LORD. Praise ye the LORD."
(Psalm 150:6, KJV)

OCTOBER 31, 2021

PRAISE GOD WITH MUSIC

PSALM 149:1–5; 150:1–6

Use with Bible Study Guide 9.

WORDS, PHRASES, AND DEFINITIONS

Write the definition of the following words.

1. Meek: ____________________
2. Firmament: ____________________
3. Hallelujah: ____________________
4. Embodied: ____________________
5. Feat: ____________________
6. Vindicate: ____________________
7. Vast expanse: ____________________
8. Repertoire: ____________________
9. Admonition: ____________________
10. Dominant message: ____________________

JUMP-STARTING THE LESSON

11. Mr. Turner wanted his daughter to play ____________________ music, but Lisa preferred to play ____________________ ____________________. (In Focus)

12. What did Mr. Turner want his daughter to get? A ____________________.

UNDERSTANDING THE LESSON

13. Check the instruments that would be used to praise God: (Focal Verses)

_____ Trumpet _____ Psaltery _____ Harp

14. Draw a line from the instrument to its description: (The People, Places, and Times)

a. Trumpet	1. Double cymbals
b. Psaltery	2. Ram's horn
c. Cymbals	3. Instrument with a twangy sound
d. Harp	4. Instrument that was plucked
e. Timbrel	5. Tambourine

15. What are Psalms 146-150 called? (Background)

____________________ ____________________

A L H L E L U H A J S A P L M S

16. What kind of psalm will need to be created for a special victory? (In Depth)

A ____________________ song

17. God finds delight in:

________________ ________________ ________________ ________________

PEOPLE HIS FOR CARING

18. What should God be praised for?

His works

Who He is

COMMITTING TO THE WORD

19. Memorize and write verbatim.

Psalm 150:6 ____

____

____

WALKING IN THE WORD

20. Choose your favorite psalm and make up a tune or choose a psalm that you already know a tune to.

Write down the title.

____

____

____

"These are they which came out of great tribulation, and have washed their robes, and made them white in the blood of the Lamb." (from Revelation 7:14, KJV)

NOVEMBER 7, 2021

ALL PEOPLE PRAISE GOD

REVELATION 7:9–17

Use with Bible Study Guide 10.

WORDS, PHRASES, AND DEFINITIONS

Write the definition of the following words.

1. Tribulation: ____________________
2. Kindred: ____________________
3. Arrayed: ____________________
4. Exiled: ____________________
5. Scroll: ____________________
6. Interlude: ____________________
7. Redeemed: ____________________
8. Mandated: ____________________
9. Garments: ____________________
10. Tabernacle: ____________________

JUMP-STARTING THE LESSON

11. What problems was Patricia facing: (In Focus)

_______ Her husband lost his job.

_______ Her mother was diagnosed with cancer.

_______ Her teenage son was rebelling.

12. What did Gladys advise Patricia to do?

_______ Ask God to help her.

_______ Praise God for being with her.

_______ Have a good cry.

UNDERSTANDING THE LESSON

13. What questions does the elder ask John? (Focal Verses)

    a. Who are these clothed in white?

    b. What are their names?

    c. Where did they come from?

14. John, the author of Revelation, was… (The People, Places, and Times)

    a. one of the apostles.

    b. the son of James.

    c. the brother of Zebedee.

    d. exiled to the island of Patmos for testifying about Jesus Christ.

15. Which are true about the scroll that God was holding? (Background)

    Only Jesus was worthy to open the seals on the scroll.

    Each time that Jesus opened a seal a judgment was visited upon the earth.

16. Revelation 7 opens during an ____________________ between the seals.

17. Underline the different kinds of people that John saw: (In Depth)

    Different races Different cultures Different languages

18. Circle the attributes of God that the choir was praising.

    Blessing Glory Wisdom Thanksgiving Honor Power Might/Strength

19. Who are those who were singing praise to God?

    Those who had ____________________ through the great tribulation.

COMMITTING TO THE WORD

20. Memorize and write verbatim.

    Revelation 7:14 ____

    ____

WALKING IN THE WORD

21. Find a praise song written in another language. Write down the title and translate as much of it as you can.

    ____

    ____

"The kingdoms of this world are become the kingdoms of our Lord, and of his Christ; and he shall reign for ever and ever." (from Revelation 11:15, KJV)

NOVEMBER 14, 2021

PRAISE FOR GOD'S ETERNAL REIGN

REVELATION 11:15–19

Use with Bible Study Guide 11.

WORDS, PHRASES, AND DEFINITIONS

Write the definition of the following words.

1. Sovereignty: ______________________________
2. Subsidiaries: ______________________________
3. Reign: ______________________________
4. Elicit fear: ______________________________
5. Unadulterated: ______________________________
6. Unhindered: ______________________________
7. Heralding: ______________________________
8. Consecrated purpose: ______________________________
9. Endeavoring: ______________________________
10. Contemporary terrestrial church: ______________________________

JUMP-STARTING THE LESSON

11. Why were the vice presidents relieved? (In Focus)

    They had a track record of ____________________ ____________________ to make the company grow.

    D A D G I N S O R E U C E S R

12. Why Phil was hopeful about the new owners?

    They had a reputation for honoring its employees'

    ____________________ - ____________________ balance.

    K O R W F E L I

UNDERSTANDING THE LESSON

13. How long shall our Lord Jesus Christ reign? (Focal Verses) ______________________________

14. Circle the things that the trumpet signals: (The People, Places, and Times)

His holiness | His righteousness | His promises | His guidance | His judgment

15. What is the actual purpose of the book of Revelation? (Background)

Unadulterated and unhindered ____________________ to the Almighty God

O R S W H I P

16. Which of these are the responsibility of the 24 elders? (In Depth)

a. ______ Their purpose is to acknowledge God.

b. ______ They submit themselves as subject to God's judgment.

c. ______ They distribute harps to all the angels.

d. ______ They begin worship with thanksgiving.

e. ______ They honor the eternal God.

17. Circle the things God uses in this passage to demonstrate His authority over all creation.

Lightning | Thunder | Earthquakes | Voices | Stock market crashes | Great hail

COMMITTING TO THE WORD

18. Memorize and write verbatim.

Revelation 11:15 ______________________________

____

____

____

WALKING IN THE WORD

19. How can you commit to exercising a lifestyle of praise and adoration to God?

____

____

____

____

"Let us be glad and rejoice, and give honour to him: for the marriage of the Lamb is come, and his wife hath made herself ready." (Revelation 19:7, KJV)

REJOICING IN HEAVEN

REVELATION 19:1–8

Use with Bible Study Guide 12.

WORDS, PHRASES, AND DEFINITIONS

Write the definition of the following words.

1. Implications: ____________________
2. Propagate: ____________________
3. Whore: ____________________
4. Fornication: ____________________
5. Avenge: ____________________
6. Omnipotent: ____________________
7. Arrayed: ____________________
8. Imagery: ____________________
9. Emblematic: ____________________
10. Marginalized: ____________________

JUMP-STARTING THE LESSON

11. What is a charging document? (In Focus)

It lists the ____________________ that the person has supposedly ____________________.

MECIRS MIMCOTEDT

12. What did Odetta pray that God would do? That ____________________ would be ____________________.

UNDERSTANDING THE LESSON

13. What momentous event is happening in this chapter? (Focal Verses)

The ____________________ of the ____________________.

ARMIAGER MBAL

14. Draw lines to the right answers: (The People, Places, and Times)

a. Who is the Bride in the Old Testament? 1. Christ

b. Who is the Bride in the New Testament? 2. Israel

c. Who is the Bridegroom in the New Testament? 3. The Church

15. What empire is symbolic of all evil empires, powers, and people? (Background) ____________________.

16. Who is the great whore/prostitute in verse 2? (In Depth) ____________________

What happened to her? God has ____________________/____________________ her.

17. How has Jesus cleaned His faithful for their marriage to Him?

Jesus ____________________ the price of our ____________________ on the ____________________.

COMMITTING TO THE WORD

18. Memorize and write verbatim.

Revelation 19:7 ____

____

____

____

WALKING IN THE WORD

19. In the end, God's justice will always prevail. What can you do today to bring about justice for this time?

____

____

____

____

"Then Peter opened his mouth, and said, Of a truth I perceive that God is no respecter of persons: But in every nation he that feareth him, and worketh righteousness, is accepted with him." (Acts 10:34–35, KJV)

NOVEMBER 28, 2021

GOOD NEWS FOR ALL

ACTS 10:34–47

Use with Bible Study Guide 13.

WORDS, PHRASES, AND DEFINITIONS

Write the definition of the following words.

1. Portrayal: ______________________________
2. Deity: ______________________________
3. Graven image: ______________________________
4. Quick and dead: ______________________________
5. Tongues: ______________________________
6. Magnify: ______________________________
7. Gentile: ______________________________
8. Adhered: ______________________________
9. Centurion: ______________________________
10. Piety: ______________________________

JUMP-STARTING THE LESSON

11. How did Kyle wish to see Jesus portrayed in the movie? (In Focus)

    Blond Norwegian   Brown-skinned Jewish Israeli   Dark Black man

12. What can portrayals of Jesus cause?

    Images can ____________________ and cause ____________________.

    VIDIDE   FUSCNOION

UNDERSTANDING THE LESSON

13. Peter preached to Cornelius that there is ______________ with God through Jesus Christ. (Focal Verses)

14. Underline the facts about Cornelius: (The People, Places, and Times)

a. He gave alms to the poor and prayed to God.

b. He was the first Gentile cited in Scripture to hear the Gospel and receive salvation.

c. He was a high-ranking army official.

d. He was a circumcised Jew.

15. Number each sentence to show the order of Peter's vision.

_______ God showed Peter many animals and told him to eat.

_______ Peter realized that God had a special message in this vision.

_______ Peter refused to eat the animals.

_______ God told Peter not to call anything unclean that He God called clean.

16. What did God teach Peter through Cornelius' conversion? (Background)

God's gift of __________________ is available to all who __________________.

ALSVTAOIN ELBIVEE

17. Unscramble the words: (In Depth)

Peter preached the __________________ __________________ of Christ to people gathered with Cornelius.

ODOG SWNE

Peter was eyewitness to the truth that Jesus came to __________________ again. ELIF

Cornelius was baptized with __________________ and with the __________________ __________________.

TWARE YLOH PIRIST

COMMITTING TO THE WORD

18. Memorize and write verbatim.

Acts 10:34–35 ____

____

____

WALKING IN THE WORD

19. Think of someone you know who is of a different ethnic background and share the Gospel with them this week. Write down the name of the person and how they responded.

____

____

"And now, Israel, what doth the LORD thy God require of thee, but to fear the LORD thy God, to walk in all his ways, and to love him, and to serve the LORD thy God with all thy heart and with all thy soul, To keep the commandments of the LORD, and his statutes, which I command thee this day for thy good?" (Deuteronomy 10:12–13, KJV)

DECEMBER 5, 2021

JUSTICE AND OBEDIENCE TO THE LAW

DEUTERONOMY 5:1–3; 10:12–13; 27:1–10

Use with Bible Study Guide 1.

WORDS, PHRASES, AND DEFINITIONS

Write the definition of the following words.

1. Statutes: ____________________
2. Covenant: ____________________
3. Plaister: ____________________
4. Burnt offerings: ____________________
5. Peace offerings: ____________________
6. Hearken: ____________________
7. Decrees: ____________________
8. Threshold: ____________________
9. Heirs: ____________________
10. Prohibitions: ____________________

JUMP-STARTING THE LESSON

11. Supply the missing word. What truth about Thomas Jefferson did Trevor bring up? (In Focus)

    Sally Hemings was not recognized as ____________________ status with himself.

12. Where did Mr. Johnson say that perfect law can be found? God's ____________________.

UNDERSTANDING THE LESSON

13. What does God require of us? (Focal Verses)

    ____________________ (EARF) the Lord thy God.

    ____________________ (LKAW) in all His ways.

_______________ (VEOL) Him.

_______________ (VESRE) the LORD thy God with all thy heart and with all thy soul.

14. Underline the sentence that is true concerning the burnt offering. (The People, Places, and Times)

    It was meant to show one's complete devotion to God.

    It was the rarest form of sacrifice.

15. Cross off the wrong word and replace it with the correct word about the Israelites. (Background)

    a. They saw five plagues on their oppressors.

    b. They saw God part the Dead Sea.

    c. They received the Twelve Commandments.

    d. They ate food from Babylon.

    e. They drank water from a waterfall.

16. What did God want from His people? (In Depth)

    God wanted a _______________ relationship with His people and for His people to have _______________ relationships with each other.

COMMITTING TO THE WORD

17. Memorize and write verbatim:

    Deuteronomy 10:12–13 _______________

WALKING IN THE WORD

18. What are some habits that would help you spiritually and that you like to learn to persevere in?

"And David said, Is there yet any that is left of the house of Saul, that I may shew him kindness for Jonathan's sake?" (2 Samuel 9:1, KJV)

DECEMBER 12, 2021

DAVID ADMINISTERS JUSTICE AND KINDNESS

2 SAMUEL 9:1–12

Use with Bible Study Guide 2.

WORDS, PHRASES, AND DEFINITIONS

Write the definition of the following words.

1. Equity: ______________________________
2. High stakes: ______________________________
3. Deployment: ______________________________
4. Shew: ______________________________
5. Art thou: ______________________________
6. Fetched: ______________________________
7. Alway: ______________________________
8. Summoned: ______________________________
9. Lame: ______________________________
10. Abnormality: ______________________________

JUMP-STARTING THE LESSON

11. What did the boys promise each other? Finish the sentence. (In Focus)

    They would always ____________ out for ____________ ____________.

12. How did Carl keep his promise? "I'll ____________ you and raise you as best I can."

UNDERSTANDING THE LESSON

13. Spell the name of Jonathan's son. (Focal Verses)

    ____________ P H I B M E O E T H S H

14. Check what is true about those who were crippled in David's time: (The People, Places, and Times)

a. ______ They became beggars.

b. ______ They were unable to work.

c. ______ People were very kind to them.

15. Cross off the wrong words and write in the correct words: (Background)

a. David and Jonathan were enemies.

b. David was next in line for the throne.

c. David forgot his friend, Jonathan.

16. David proved himself to be a ____________________ and ____________________ king. (In Depth)

17. Circle the word that does not answer the question. How did Mephibosheth feel appearing before King David?

Humble Afraid Angry

18. Which did David do for Mephibosheth?

a. He gave him Saul's ancestral lands.

b. He appointed Ziba to care for the lands.

c. Mephibosheth's son would carry on his name.

COMMITTING TO THE WORD

19. Memorize and write verbatim:

2 Samuel 9:1 ____

____

____

____

WALKING IN THE WORD

20. How can you show radical kindness to someone in need this week?

____

____

____

____

____

> *"Of the increase of his government and peace there shall be no end, upon the throne of David, and upon his kingdom, to order it, and to establish it with judgment and with justice from henceforth even for ever. The zeal of the LORD of hosts will perform this." (Isaiah 9:7, KJV)*

DECEMBER 19, 2021

JUSTICE AND RIGHTEOUSNESS REIGN

ISAIAH 9:2–7

Use with Bible Study Guide 3.

WORDS, PHRASES, AND DEFINITIONS

Write the definition of the following words.

1. Commodity: ____________________
2. Stablish: ____________________
3. Divide the spoil: ____________________
4. Yoke of his burden: ____________________
5. Staff: ____________________
6. Rod of his oppressor: ____________________
7. Garments rolled in blood: ____________________
8. Turbulent: ____________________
9. Vassal state: ____________________
10. Tribute: ____________________

JUMP-STARTING THE LESSON

11. Contrast Taneisha and Maxine's appreciation for their holiday trip: (In Focus)

    Taneisha was ____________________, and Maxine valued ____________________ and ____________________.

12. Only Jesus can help us experience ____________________ and lasting ____________________.

UNDERSTANDING THE LESSON

13. Unscramble the titles of Jesus: (Focal Verses)

    ____________________(O N D W R E U L F) ____________________(N S L E L O C U O R)

The ____________________ (H G I M T Y) ____________________ (D G O)

The ____________________ (V R E L E A T N G I) ____________________ (H E F A T R)

____________________ (I N R P C E) of ____________________ (C E P A E)

14. Which are true about Isaiah? (The People, Places, and Times)

    a. ______ He ministered for 48 years.

    b. ______ He saw fellow citizens taken into captivity.

    c. ______ He prophesied during the reign of Uzziah, Jotham, Ahaz, Hezekiah, and Manasseh.

    d. ______ His wife was a prophetess.

    e. ______ He had only one son.

15. Why did Isaiah criticize the people of Judah? (Background)

    Their sinfulness and unwillingness to be ____________________ to the one true God.

16. Fill in the missing words: (In Depth)

    a. Darkness and dwelling in the land of the shadow of death is ____________________.

    b. Isaiah prophesied that the great light, ____________________ ____________________ would appear.

17. Fill in the words:

    a. The Messiah would be heir to the ____________________ throne.

    b. The Prince of Peace will ____________________ peace and will ____________________ with peace.

COMMITTING TO THE WORD

18. Memorize and write verbatim:

    Isaiah 9:7 ____

    ____

    ____

WALKING IN THE WORD

19. Who can you share with this week that Jesus is the hope of eternal peace and justice?

    ____

    ____

"And when they were come into the house, they saw the young child with Mary his mother, and fell down, and worshipped him: and when they had opened their treasures, they presented unto him gifts; gold, and frankincense and myrrh."
(Matthew 2:11, KJV)

DECEMBER 26, 2021

A JUST KING IS BORN

MATTHEW 2:1–12

Use with Bible Study Guide 4.

WORDS, PHRASES, AND DEFINITIONS

Write the definition of the following words.

1. Inclusion: ______________________________
2. Marginalized: ______________________________
3. Vulnerable: ______________________________
4. Frankincense: ______________________________
5. Myrrh: ______________________________
6. Privily: ______________________________
7. Diligently: ______________________________
8. Magi: ______________________________
9. Tremendous architectural feats: ______________________________
10. Paranoia: ______________________________

JUMP-STARTING THE LESSON

11. Who was Edward trying to help? Unscramble the words: (In Focus)

    ____________________(M E H O S E L S) ____________________(M I M I G A N R T)

12. What did Edward see that came to interrupt his help?

    ____________________(M I M I T O I N A G R) van

UNDERSTANDING THE LESSON

13. Look at both translations and circle the words concerning who is predicted to come from Bethlehem.

    (Focal Verses) Governor Ruler King

14. Underline information about the magi: (The People, Places, and Times)

   a. They probably came from Persia (modern-day Iran).

   b. They were astrologers.

   c. They came riding on horses or camels.

   d. There were only three of them.

15. Underline the information about King Herod the Great: (Background)

   a. He was a Jewish king working on behalf of Rome.

   b. He renovated the Third Temple in Jerusalem.

   c. He lowered the taxes.

   d. He murdered several of his own children and wives.

16. Fill in the name: (In Depth)

   Matthew traced the ancestors of Jesus back to King ____________________.

17. Where did the religious leaders say that the Messiah would be born? ____________________

18. The wise men went back ____________________ (N O A H T E R) way.

COMMITTING TO THE WORD

19. Memorize and write verbatim:

   Matthew 2:11 ____

   ____

   ____

   ____

   ____

WALKING IN THE WORD

20. The wise men performed an act of civil disobedience by not returning to King Herod. What act of civil disobedience could you perform?

   ____

   ____

   ____

   ____

   ____

"And he said, What hast thou done? the voice of thy brother's blood crieth unto me from the ground." (Genesis 4:10, KJV)

JANUARY 2, 2022

JUSTICE, VENGEANCE, AND MERCY

GENESIS 4:1–16

Use with Bible Study Guide 5.

WORDS, PHRASES, AND DEFINITIONS

Write the definition of the following words.

1. Bear the brunt: ____________________
2. Deluged: ____________________
3. God's grace sustained: ____________________
4. Tiller of the ground: ____________________
5. Firstlings of the flock: ____________________
6. Wroth: ____________________
7. Fugitive: ____________________
8. Vagabond: ____________________
9. Slay: ____________________
10. Vengeance: ____________________

JUMP-STARTING THE LESSON

11. What was Reginald's big problem? (In Focus)

    A bad ____________________.

12. What two things did Reginald do to improve his life?

    a. Working through his ____________________.

    b. Committing his life to ____________________.

UNDERSTANDING THE LESSON

13. What did God tell Cain would rule over him, if he did not subdue it? (Focal Verses) ________________

14. Write the word that goes with the definition: (The People, Places, and Times)

    a. ____________________ means the oldest child

    b. ____________________ means the best and first of the crop

15. Write the name of the brother in the correct blank: (Background)

    a. ____________________ gave his best to please the Lord.

    b. ____________________ did not give his best, but wanted God's favor.

16. Whom did Cain direct his anger toward? (In Depth) ____________________

17. What was Cain's answer to God's question, "Where is Abel thy brother?" ____________________________

    ____

18. Why was Cain's sin not pardoned?

    Cain had no desire to __________________ (P E R E N T) or ____________________ (C N R E O C L I E).

COMMITTING TO THE WORD

19. Memorize and write verbatim:

    Genesis 4:10 ____

    ____

    ____

    ____

    ____

    ____

WALKING IN THE WORD

20. Try to think of something that you need to repent of and ask God to forgive you.

    ____

    ____

    ____

    ____

    ____

"And God heard the voice of the lad; and the angel of God called to Hagar out of heaven, and said unto her, What aileth thee, Hagar? fear not; for God hath heard the voice of the lad where he is. Arise, lift up the lad, and hold him in thine hand; for I will make him a great nation." (Genesis 21:17–18, KJV)

JANUARY 9, 2022

HAGAR AND ISHMAEL NOT FORGOTTEN

GENESIS 21:8–20

Use with Bible Study Guide 6.

WORDS, PHRASES, AND DEFINITIONS

Write the definition of the following words.

1. Aileth: ______________________________
2. Descendants: ______________________________
3. Weaned: ______________________________
4. Cast: ______________________________
5. Bondwoman: ______________________________
6. Hearken: ______________________________
7. Bow shot: ______________________________
8. Archer: ______________________________
9. Hostility: ______________________________
10. Turmoil: ______________________________

JUMP-STARTING THE LESSON

11. Underline the two things that Carol wished concerning her father? (In Focus)

    a. That he would take a greater interest in her.

    b. That he would attend church with her.

    c. That he would visit her mother.

12. Fill in the missing words. Carol graduated from ____________________ with ____________________.

UNDERSTANDING THE LESSON

13. How did God show mercy to Ishmael? (Focal Verses)

    God was ____________________ him as he grew up.

14. Which are true about the Wilderness of Paran? (The People, Places, and Times)

a. ______ It is in the southeast section of the Sinai Peninsula.

b. ______ It has very little rainfall.

c. ______ The 12 Israelite scouts entered the Promised Land from here.

d. ______ King David spent some time hiding from Saul here.

15. An angel appeared to Hagar the first time she ran away. What did he tell her then? (Background)

a. The angel told her to run to Egypt.

b. The angel told her to call her child Ishmael.

c. The angel said God hears her affliction.

16. Which is the child of promise? (In Depth)

Ishmael Isaac

17. How did God comfort Abraham? He promised him that He would also ____________________ Ishmael.

18. How did Hagar approach the possible death of her son from thirst? She moved away from him and she began to ____________________.

19. How did God respond to Hagar?

a. He called her by name.

b. He told her not to fear.

c. He heard the voice of her son.

d. He showed her a well of water.

e. Ishmael's descendants would soon be forgotten.

COMMITTING TO THE WORD

20. Memorize and write verbatim:

Genesis 21:17–18 ____

____

____

WALKING IN THE WORD

21. Write a prayer telling God you are trusting Him in the midst of your current problems.

____

____

"Thou shalt not follow a multitude to do evil; neither shalt thou speak in a cause to decline after many to wrest judgment: Neither shalt thou countenance a poor man in his cause."
(Exodus 23:2–3, KJV)

JANUARY 16, 2022

THE LAWS OF JUSTICE AND MERCY

EXODUS 23:1–12

Use with Bible Study Guide 7.

WORDS, PHRASES, AND DEFINITIONS

Write the definition of the following words.

1. Renegotiate: ____________________
2. Impartial: ____________________
3. Wrest judgment: ____________________
4. Put not thine hand with the wicked: ____________________
5. Take no gift: ____________________
6. Do not oppress a stranger: ____________________
7. Sow thy land: ____________________
8. Son of the handmaid: ____________________
9. Covenant: ____________________
10. Imperative: ____________________

JUMP-STARTING THE LESSON

11. Why was Toni helping Binta? (In Focus)

    She wanted her neighborhood to be ____________ and ____________.

12. How did Toni help Binta?

    She looked over the ____________ and helped her renegotiate it with the

    ____________.

UNDERSTANDING THE LESSON

13. Look at verses 3 and 6 in the NLT and underline how the poor should be treated in court: (Focal Verses)

a. Do not favor a person because that person is poor.

b. Do not deny justice to the poor.

c. Give the poor person the benefit of the doubt.

14. What non-legal terms are included in God's hatred of lying? (The People, Places, and Times)

____________________ (O S G G S P I), ____________________ (D R S A L N E)

15. What does Exodus 20:22–23:33 expand upon? (Background) The Ten ____________________

16. Underline five commands from verses 1 through 3: (In Depth)

a. Don't pass along false rumors.

b. Don't make your donkey work on the Sabbath.

c. Don't cooperate with evil by lying on the witness stand.

d. Don't show favoritism to the poor.

e. Don't follow the crowd in doing wrong.

f. Don't wear white after Labor Day.

g. Don't twist justice.

17. The just person must help in all situations, whether the person needing help is a ____________________ or a ____________________.

18. Why are bribes forbidden? Bribes ____________________ judges to justice.

19. Underline the good that comes about due to honoring the Sabbath year.

a. Farmers are compelled to rely on God's grace, which strengthens their faith.

b. The Sabbath year provides food for the poor.

c. The Sabbath provides a rest for all.

COMMITTING TO THE WORD

20. Memorize and write verbatim:

Exodus 23:2–3 ____

____

WALKING IN THE WORD

21. How can you help someone in need this week? Write down your answer.

____

____

"Judges and officers shalt thou make thee in all thy gates, which the LORD thy God giveth thee, throughout thy tribes: and they shall judge the people with just judgment." (Deuteronomy 16:18, KJV)

JANUARY 23, 2022

JUSTICE, JUDGES, AND PRIESTS

DEUTERONOMY 16:18–20; 17:8–13

Use with Bible Study Guide 8.

WORDS, PHRASES, AND DEFINITIONS

Write the definition of the following words.

1. Entailed: ______________________________
2. Collaborative environment: ______________________________
3. Galvanize: ______________________________
4. Integrity: ______________________________
5. Invested: ______________________________
6. Aligned with his values: ______________________________
7. Wrest judgment: ______________________________
8. Verdict: ______________________________
9. Purge the evil: ______________________________
10. Cumbersome: ______________________________

JUMP-STARTING THE LESSON

11. What did the new pastor want to help bring about in his new church? (In Focus)

    He wanted the community to work ____________________.

12. Why did Alderman Johnson want to serve the community with integrity? Because he was a

    ____________________-follower.

UNDERSTANDING THE LESSON

13. Match the phrases from the KJV with those from the NLT. (Focal Verses)

KJV	NLT
a. Judge the people with fair judgment.	1. Twist justice.
b. Wrest judgment.	2. Declare the verdict.
c. Shew thee the sentence of judgment.	3. Judge the people fairly.

14. Why did God say "the place the Lord your God will choose"? Circle the right word in the parentheses. (The People, Places, and Times)

 a. The (Tabernacle Temple) was in several places.

 b. The people worshiped in the Temple in (Jerusalem Bethlehem).

15. Why did God give such detailed laws for His people? Fill in the missing words: (Background)

 They were to be an ____________________ to the other nations of God's ____________________ and ____________________ by administering ____________________ as a civil society.

16. Who would advise the official in difficult cases? (In Depth) ______________________________

COMMITTING TO THE WORD

17. Memorize and write verbatim:

 Deuteronomy 16:18 ____

 ____

 ____

 ____

WALKING IN THE WORD

18. Think of a decision you will need to make this week. How can you use God's Word to help you make that decision justly?

 ____

 ____

 ____

 ____

> "But thou shalt remember that thou wast a bondman in Egypt, and the LORD thy God redeemed thee thence: therefore I command thee to do this thing." (Deuteronomy 24:18, KJV)

JANUARY 30, 2022

JUSTICE AND THE MARGINALIZED

DEUTERONOMY 24:10–21

Use with Bible Study Guide 9.

WORDS, PHRASES, AND DEFINITIONS

Write the definition of the following words.

1. Disenfranchised: ______________________________
2. Fetch his pledge: ______________________________
3. Raiment: ______________________________
4. Bondman: ______________________________
5. Redeemed thee from thence: ______________________________
6. Sheaf: ______________________________
7. Beatest thine olive tree: ______________________________
8. Glean: ______________________________
9. Destitute laborers: ______________________________
10. Absolved: ______________________________

JUMP-STARTING THE LESSON

11. What bad luck had happened to Melissa? (In Focus)

    She was ____________ ____________ from the company she worked for.

12. What did her brother say to encourage her?

    a. God has a purpose.

    b. Look on the bright side!

    c. God has your back.

    d. Our church has a program that might be just what you need.

UNDERSTANDING THE LESSON

13. Look at verses 19, 20, and 21 and write down the three groups of people that should be able to pick up leftover farm crops. (Focal Verses)

    a. ______________________________

    b. ______________________________

    c. ______________________________

14. Which are true about the book of Deuteronomy? (The People, Places, and Times)

    a. It is quoted in the New Testament 40 times.

    b. Jesus quoted it when tempted by Satan.

    c. Jesus quoted the greatest commandment from it.

15. The remainder of chapter 24 fixes on preserving the ____________________ of the poor. (Background)

16. Fill in the words to show how the debtor and the creditor were to treat each other: (In Depth)

    a. The debtor must show his ____________________ to pay.

    b. The creditor should trust the ____________________ of the debtor.

17. What does verse 16 seek to eliminate? ____________________ actions.

18. When the privileged have surplus crops, whom should it be preserved for? The ____________________.

COMMITTING TO THE WORD

19. Memorize and write verbatim:

    Deuteronomy 24:18 ____

    ____

    ____

    ____

WALKING IN THE WORD

20. What can you do this week to share love with those who are rejected by others?

    ____

    ____

    ____

    ____

"And Nathan said to David, Thou art the man." (from 2 Samuel 12:7, KJV)

NATHAN CONDEMNS DAVID

2 SAMUEL 12:1–9, 13–15

Use with Bible Study Guide 10.

WORDS, PHRASES, AND DEFINITIONS

Write the definition of the following words.

1. Ewe lamb: ____________________
2. Bosom: ____________________
3. Dressed: ____________________
4. Kindled: ____________________
5. Fourfold: ____________________
6. Howbeit: ____________________
7. Ironically: ____________________
8. Not exempt from the consequences: ____________________
9. God's omniscient view: ____________________
10. Curry favor: ____________________

JUMP-STARTING THE LESSON

11. Underline the correct reasons. Why was Carlton everyone's pet? (In Focus)

    a. He was a good student.

    b. He was the baby of the family.

    c. He never did wrong.

12. What does the younger generation need to learn? Fill in the missing word.

    To face the ____________________.

UNDERSTANDING THE LESSON

13. What did the rich man have? (Focal Verses) A great many ____________________ (H E S E P)

What did the poor man have? One ewe ____________________ (M A L B)

14. Draw lines from the description to the name: (The People, Places, and Times)

a. A faithful prophet and trusted advisor — David

b. The youngest son

c. Became the king — Nathan

d. Did not curry favor

15. Unscramble the missing words: (Background)

a. David understood the story of the lamb, because he was a ____________________. (H E S H E R D P)

b. God is our Shepherd, but no one can ____________________ us from His hand. (L U P K C)

16. Underline how God revealed to David his sin: (In Depth)

a. Nathan used a parable.

b. God sent a plague on Israel.

c. Nathan spoke to David of a vision he had.

17. Fill in the missing words.

a. There is no remission of sin without ____________________.

b. There is no repentance without an acknowledgment of ____________________.

18. What were David's most important words?

I have ____________________ against the ____________________.

COMMITTING TO THE WORD

19. Memorize and write verbatim:

2 Samuel 12:7 ____

____

WALKING IN THE WORD

20. Write down which of these three things you need to do now: Admit your sins; ask God's forgiveness; make godly choices.

____

____

____

"For Ezra had prepared his heart to seek the law of the LORD, and to do it, and to teach in Israel statutes and judgments." (Ezra 7:10, KJV)

EZRA SEEKS GOD'S LAW

EZRA 7:1–10, 23–26

Use with Bible Study Guide 11.

WORDS, PHRASES, AND DEFINITIONS

Write the definition of the following words.

1. Insurmountable: ____________________
2. Statutes: ____________________
3. Judgments: ____________________
4. Decrees: ____________________
5. Scribe in the law of Moses: ____________________
6. Granted: ____________________
7. Priests: ____________________
8. Levites: ____________________
9. Porters: ____________________
10. Nethinims: ____________________

JUMP-STARTING THE LESSON

11. What terrible thing had happened to Pastor Joel's church? (In Focus)

    A ____________ swept ____________ away.

12. What two things did Pastor Joel say that they could do?

    a. Rebuild the ____________ of our ____________.

    b. Organize a community-wide ____________ of ____________.

UNDERSTANDING THE LESSON

13. Why did King Artaxerxes give Ezra everything he requested? (Focal Verses)

    The gracious hand of the Lord his God was ____________ him.

14. Write down the names of the kings that ruled while the Israelites were building or stopping their building: (The People, Places, and Times)

C_____________ the Great, King D_____________, King X_____________, King A_____________.

15. Number the events in order: (Background)

a. ______ King Cyrus defeated the Babylonians.

b. ______ Zerubbabel led the rebuilding of the Temple.

c. ______ Cyrus allowed people to return to their homelands.

d. ______ Ezra established the Torah as the governing laws of Jerusalem.

16. Underline Ezra's qualifications: (In Depth)

a. Descended from Aaron, the first high priest

b. Educated in the history of his people

c. Qualified to interpret and teach God's Law

17. What two other important qualities did Ezra possess?

a. Love for the Word of God

b. A handsome face

c. Desire that others would love and obey the ways of the Lord

18. How did God honor the desire of Ezra's heart?

a. ______ He gave him favor with King Artaxerxes.

b. ______ Royal decree for safe passage.

c. ______ Provinces were commanded to supply the material needs.

d. ______ He appointed Ezra to govern the people according to God's Law.

COMMITTING TO THE WORD

19. Memorize and write verbatim:

Ezra 7:10 ____

____

WALKING IN THE WORD

20. Write some notes of thanks to those who teach you God's Word.

____

____

"Then answered Bildad the Shuhite, and said, How long wilt thou speak these things? and how long shall the words of thy mouth be like a strong wind?" (Job 8:1–2, KJV)

FEBRUARY 20, 2022

BILDAD MISUNDERSTANDS GOD'S JUSTICE

JOB 8:1–10, 20–22

Use with Bible Study Guide 12.

WORDS, PHRASES, AND DEFINITIONS

Write the definition of the following words.

1. Grated on him: ______________________
2. Pervert justice: ______________________
3. Transgression: ______________________
4. Betimes: ______________________
5. Supplication to the Almighty: ______________________
6. Make the habitation of thy righteousness prosperous: ______________________
7. Though thy beginning was small: ______________________
8. Thy latter end should greatly increase: ______________________
9. Dwelling place of the wicked shall come to nought: ______________________
10. Theodicy: ______________________

JUMP-STARTING THE LESSON

11. In spite of her cancer, what did Angela do every day? (In Focus) She ______________________ God.
12. What was Tim's question? "How could God ______________________ ______________________

    to my wife?"

UNDERSTANDING THE LESSON

13. Bildad asked, "Does God pervert/twist ______________________?" (Focal Verses)

14. Cross out the wrong answers to why bad things happened to good people: (The People, Places, and Times)

a. God is not powerful enough to prevent bad things.

b. God does not care what happens to us.

c. God is not just.

d. God cares and He can help us.

15. Put a check in front of what Job had lost: (Background)

a. ______ His children

b. ______ His wealth

c. ______ His devotion to God

16. What four things was Bildad convinced of? (In Depth)

a. God is perfectly and always ____________________.

b. A just God will always ____________________ sin.

c. A just God will always bless the ____________________.

d. A just God will always restore the ____________________.

COMMITTING TO THE WORD

17. Memorize and write verbatim:

Job 8:1–2 ____

____

____

____

WALKING IN THE WORD

18. Look at some Christian TV shows this week and find some things that agree with Bildad, rather than God's just ways.

____

____

____

____

"Who is he that hideth counsel without knowledge? therefore have I uttered that I understood not; things too wonderful for me, which I knew not." (Job 42:3, KJV)

FEBRUARY 27, 2022

SERVING A JUST GOD

JOB 42:1–6, 10–17

Use with Bible Study Guide 13.

WORDS, PHRASES, AND DEFINITIONS

Write the definition of the following words.

1. Hideth counsel: ____________________
2. Abhor: ____________________
3. Turned the captivity: ____________________
4. Fair: ____________________
5. Oddly archaic: ____________________
6. Prologue: ____________________
7. Epilogue: ____________________
8. Appease God: ____________________
9. Preempts: ____________________
10. Nuanced: ____________________

JUMP-STARTING THE LESSON

11. Why was Carrie unjustly put in prison? (In Focus)

    An officer planted ____________________ in her jacket.

12. Where did Carrie find help after she got out of prison?

    ____________________ Johnson at her old ____________________.

UNDERSTANDING THE LESSON

13. Previously Job had known about God through what he had heard. How does he say he knows God now?

    (Focal Verses) He saw God with his own ____________________.

14. Write the number in front of each description of a part of the book of Job in the proper order: (The People, Places, and Times)

_______ Poetry

_______ Epilogue

_______ Prologue

15. Fill in the words to define theodicy: (Background)

If God is loving and just, why did He allow such __________________ and degradation in the life of __________________ Job?

16. Job discovered the omniscience of God. Unscramble the definition of this word: (In Depth)

God knows __________________ (V E R E H N G I T Y).

17. Job proclaims that the __________________ (A S E L O N P R) revelation of God is far more excellent than the __________________ (T I R N E P P E C O) of God.

18. What happened when Job prayed for his friends?

God restored his __________________ (O R F U N E S T).

19. How does God prove His faithfulness in our lives?

Surviving __________________ (D V A E S R T I Y)

COMMITTING TO THE WORD

20. Memorize and write verbatim:

Job 42:3 ____

____

____

WALKING IN THE WORD

21. Have you tried to blame a friend for their troubles rather than listening to them and trying to see what God is doing in their lives? How can you work this week to make amends with that person?

____

____

____

____

"And some of the chief of the fathers, when they came to the house of the LORD which is at Jerusalem, offered freely for the house of God to set it up in his place." (Ezra 2:68, KJV)

MARCH 6, 2022

BABYLONIAN CAPTIVITY ENDS

EZRA 1:1–8, 11; 2:64–70

Use with Bible Study Guide 1.

WORDS, PHRASES, AND DEFINITIONS

Write the definition of the following words.

1. Feasible: ______________________________
2. Proclamation: ______________________________
3. He hath charged me: ______________________________
4. Sojourneth: ______________________________
5. Beasts: ______________________________
6. Freewill offering: ______________________________
7. Captives: ______________________________
8. Asses: ______________________________
9. Threescore: ______________________________
10. Dram: ______________________________

JUMP-STARTING THE LESSON

11. Why did the leaders want to build a new facility? (In Focus)

The walls were ____________________, the foundation was ____________________, the stairs had begun ____________________, and the building was too ____________________.

12. What was the most important thing for the committee to do? ____________________

UNDERSTANDING THE LESSON

13. Who prophesied that King Cyrus of Persia would stir up the people to rebuild the Temple? (Focal Verses)

____

14. What did King Nebuchadnezzar do? Check all that apply. (The People, Places, and Times)

a. ______ He took many people captive to Babylon.

b. ______ He destroyed the city of Jerusalem.

c. ______ He took the silver-plated things from the king's palace.

15. What did King Cyrus do? Check all that apply.

a. ______ He captured the city of Babylon.

b. ______ He allowed the Babylonian people to return to Jerusalem.

c. ______ He allowed the Israelites to rebuild the Temple.

16. Why had the Israelites been taken into captivity? (Background)

____________________ ____________________ against God

ERSEH LERBELNIO

17. Match the answers with the questions: (In Depth)

a. Whose heart did God stir up?	Construction of the Temple
b. What did Cyrus proclaim?	Cyrus
c. How did the Israelites respond to Cyrus's proclamation?	Hearts willing to answer God's call
d. What did the exiles give gifts for?	God appointed him to rebuild the Temple

COMMITTING TO THE WORD

18. Memorize and write verbatim:

Ezra 2:68 ____

____

____

____

WALKING IN THE WORD

19. What are some situations in which you will have to trust God this week?

____

____

____

____

> *"And the God that hath caused his name to dwell there destroy all kings and people, that shall put to their hand to alter and to destroy this house of God which is at Jerusalem. I Darius have made a decree; let it be done with speed."*
> *(Ezra 6:12, KJV)*

MARCH 13, 2022

FREEDOM TO WORSHIP

EZRA 6:1-12

Use with Bible Study Guide 2.

WORDS, PHRASES, AND DEFINITIONS

Write the definition of the following words.

1. Pivotal: ____________________
2. Postpartum: ____________________
3. Alter: ____________________
4. Decree: ____________________
5. Violates: ____________________
6. Diligence: ____________________
7. Rolls: ____________________
8. Bullocks: ____________________
9. Savours: ____________________
10. Dunghill: ____________________

JUMP-STARTING THE LESSON

11. What did Maddie and Erica know they would be doing for each other? Finish each word. (In Focus)

    ____________ing, ____________ing, and ____________ing.

12. What did Maddie suggest Erica do?

    See a ____________ (C O T D O R).

UNDERSTANDING THE LESSON

13. What was in the document King Darius found? Circle the KJV word: (Focal Verses)

    a. Let the Temple be (rebuilt, builded).

b. Let the expenses be out of the (king's house, royal treasury).

c. The vessels which Nebuchadnezzar took be (restored, put back where they belong).

14. Put the correct name in the blank: (The People, Places, and Times)

a. ____________________ was the governor of Samaria and Judah.

b. ____________________ was the king of Persia at this time.

15. Who resisted the rebuilding of the Temple? Check all that apply. (Background)

a. ______ Those left in the city during the exile

b. ______ Samaritans who lived nearby

c. ______ Persians

d. ______ Enemies of Judah

16. What was King Darius known for? Check all that apply. (In Depth)

a. ______ He allowed the Jews to return to Judah and rebuild their Temple.

b. ______ He allowed his subjects to worship their own gods.

c. ______ He did not want laws written down.

17. King Darius ordered his ____________________ and other ____________________ in the region to leave the Jews alone.

18. Name two additional things King Darius did for the returning exiles.

a. He made sure they had ____________________ to offer to the Lord.

b. He warned that those who tried to stop the Jews would be ____________________.

COMMITTING TO THE WORD

19. Memorize and write verbatim:

Ezra 6:12 ____

____

WALKING IN THE WORD

20. Record a time God helped you complete a difficult project.

____

____

"And the children of Israel, the priests, and the Levites, and the rest of the children of the captivity, kept the dedication of this house of God with joy." (Ezra 6:16, KJV)

MARCH 20, 2022

CELEBRATE PASSOVER LIBERATION

EZRA 6:13–22

Use with Bible Study Guide 3.

WORDS, PHRASES, AND DEFINITIONS

Write the definition of the following words.

1. Prevailed: ______________________________
2. Rams: ______________________________
3. Unintentional sins: ______________________________
4. Bronze laver: ______________________________
5. Molten sea: ______________________________
6. Trans-Euphrates: ______________________________
7. Reinstituting: ______________________________
8. Divine intervention: ______________________________
9. Unleavened bread: ______________________________
10. Procrastinate: ______________________________

JUMP-STARTING THE LESSON

11. What difficulties did Pastor Perry and his congregation encounter in building a new church? Circle all that apply. (In Focus)

    Other obstacles   Village approval   Finding a famous architect

12. How did the congregation respond to the village approval?

    ______________   ______________

    V E R O N E Y E   J O R E C E D I

UNDERSTANDING THE LESSON

13. Who obeyed the command of King Darius? Circle all that apply. (Focal Verses)

Hezekiah | Tatnai | Shetharboznai

14. Match the three kings to their descriptions: (The People, Places, and Times)

a. Solomon | 1. Sponsored building the second Temple
b. Herod | 2. Sponsored building the first Temple
c. Darius | 3. Sponsored significant Temple renovations

15. Fill in the answers: (Background)

a. Who gave the original decree for the Temple to be built? King ___________________

b. Who made the search for the original decree? King ___________________

16. What did the people do when the Temple was completed? (In Depth)

They ___________________ it with great ___________________.

17. What did the people do next?

They offered many animals as a ___________________ for their ___________________.

18. What two feasts were celebrated?

___________________ meal

Feast of Unleavened ___________________.

COMMITTING TO THE WORD

19. Memorize and write verbatim:

Ezra 6:16 ____

____

____

____

WALKING IN THE WORD

20. Plan a banquet to celebrate the Good News of God's love.

____

____

"Beware that thou forget not the LORD thy God, in not keeping his commandments, and his judgments, and his statutes, which I command thee this day." *(Deuteronomy 8:11, KJV)*

MARCH 27, 2022

LEST WE FORGET

DEUTERONOMY 8:1–11

Use with Bible Study Guide 4.

WORDS, PHRASES, AND DEFINITIONS

Write the definition of the following words.

1. Humility: ______
2. Beware: ______
3. Sware: ______
4. Raiment: ______
5. Waxed not old: ______
6. Proceedeth out of the mouth: ______
7. Chasteneth his son: ______
8. Scarceness: ______
9. Sustain: ______
10. Polarize politics: ______

JUMP-STARTING THE LESSON

11. What did Jimmy give his basement customers? (In Focus)

A fresh ______ and ______.

TCU VADICE

12. What did Jimmy tell his customers when he opened his own shop?

______ ______

NHAKT OUY

UNDERSTANDING THE LESSON

13. Which things did God take care of in the wilderness? Check all that apply. (Focal Verses)

_______ Manna for food

_______ Clothes that did not wear out

_______ Feet that did not swell, in spite of walking long distances, over many years

_______ Red wine

14. Whenever the people met with adversity what did the people do? (The People, Places, and Times)

They ____________________ instead of praying.

P L C O M A I N D E

15. Why was Moses retelling God's Law to the Children of Israel? (Background)

This was a new ____________________ who had not experienced the things their parents had.

E N G R A I N O E T

16. What were the Israelites supposed to keep? (In Depth)

The ____________________ Commandments and many other commandments

17. Draw lines to the correct sentence ending:

a. God is a provider	1. They will face discipline.
b. Fearing God means to	2. Respect Him.
c. If His people do not obey the Lord	3. But also a parent to His followers.

18. Which things would the Israelites have available to them in the Promised Land? Circle all that apply.

fertile soil   natural fruit   abundant water sources   mineral wealth

COMMITTING TO THE WORD

19. Memorize and write verbatim:

Deuteronomy 8:11 ____

____

WALKING IN THE WORD

20. How can we remind ourselves to be humble, keep our leaders accountable, and resist the pride of nationalism?

____

____

"But I say unto you, I will not drink henceforth of this fruit of the vine, until that day when I drink it new with you in my Father's kingdom." (Matthew 26:29, KJV)

APRIL 3, 2022

THE PASSOVER WITH THE DISCIPLES

MATTHEW 26:17-30

Use with Bible Study Guide 5.

WORDS, PHRASES, AND DEFINITIONS

Write the definition of the following words.

1. Perspective: ____________________
2. Unleavened bread: ____________________
3. Passover: ____________________
4. Remission of sins: ____________________
5. Testament: ____________________
6. Covenant: ____________________
7. Mark my words: ____________________
8. Messianic title: ____________________
9. The elect: ____________________
10. Provisional victory: ____________________

JUMP-STARTING THE LESSON

11. How did Brittany feel when she saw the cross her mother wore on a chain around her neck? (In Focus)

    The pain was ____________________ (N B U E A B R L E A)

12. What did the pastor say the Cross represented? New ____________________ (F E L I) in

    ____________________ (H R I C T S).

UNDERSTANDING THE LESSON

13. Translate these KJV terms into contemporary English: (Focal Verses)

a. Where wilt thou	1. Where will you
b. Saith	2. Your, you
c. Thy, ye	3. Says

d. Even 4. Broke

e. Verily 5. Goes

f. Dippeth 6. Truly

g. Goeth 7. Evening

h. Brake 8. Dips

14. What is the significance of the term "Son of Man"? Check all that apply. (The People, Places, and Times)

a. ______ Prophecy from Daniel c. ______ Messianic title

b. ______ A title for Jesus d. ______ Title given to Jesus by His disciples

15. Which are true about Judas? Check all that apply.

a. ______ One of the 12 disciples c. ______ Managed the treasury for the group

b. ______ Last name Iscariot d. ______ Betrayed Jesus

16. The Passover represented their __________________ from Egypt's __________________.

(Background) ILBEARTNIO PEOPRSISON

17. Number each action to show the sequence. (In Depth)

______ Jesus told Judas that he would betray Him.

______ Jesus told the disciples to prepare the Passover meal.

______ Jesus said that the wine represented His blood.

______ They sang a hymn and went to the Mount of Olives.

______ Jesus said that the bread represented His body.

______ Jesus said He would next drink wine with them in His Father's Kingdom.

COMMITTING TO THE WORD

18. Memorize and write verbatim.

Matthew 26:29 ____

____

WALKING IN THE WORD

19. What will you meditate upon the next time you partake of the Lord's Supper?

____

____

"Tell ye the daughter of Sion, Behold, thy King cometh unto thee, meek, and sitting upon an ass, and a colt the foal of an ass." (Matthew 21:5, KJV)

TRIUMPHAL ENTRY INTO JERUSALEM

MATTHEW 21:1–11

Use with Bible Study Guide 6.

WORDS, PHRASES, AND DEFINITIONS

Write the definition of the following words.

1. Nomad: ______________________________
2. Triumphal Entry: ______________________________
3. Drew nigh: ______________________________
4. Any man say ought: ______________________________
5. Daughter of Sion: ______________________________
6. Foal of an ass: ______________________________
7. Strawed them: ______________________________
8. Hosanna: ______________________________
9. Procession: ______________________________
10. Replete: ______________________________

JUMP-STARTING THE LESSON

11. Which two things were part of the Hills family Easter tradition? Check all that apply. (In Focus)

    a. ______ The family attended church together.

    b. ______ The family had Easter dinner together.

    c. ______ The family wore brand-new clothes.

12. What was Marie thankful for? Check all that apply.

    a. ______ She gave thanks for Jesus.

    b. ______ She was thankful that the family listened to her.

    c. ______ She was grateful that Nana's love for God and family would live on.

UNDERSTANDING THE LESSON

13. What did the prophet say about the Triumphal Entry? (Focal Verses)

    Behold (Look), your ____________________ is coming.

14. What two anointed offices did the Messiah hold? (The People, Places, and Times)

    King Carpenter Priest Shepherd

15. Which facts emphasize the significance of Jesus' entry into Jerusalem? Check all that apply. (Background)

    a. ______ All four Gospel writers make a record of it.

    b. ______ Over 2 million people were present for the Passover.

    c. ______ Jesus came to be the ultimate sacrifice.

    d. ______ The people expected the Messiah to ride in on a camel.

16. What is the significance of Jesus riding on a donkey? (In Depth)

    It demonstrated His ____________________ (U T Y H M L I I).

17. How did the crowd identify Jesus?

    He was the ____________________ (R P H P E T O) of Nazareth.

COMMITTING TO THE WORD

18. Memorize and write verbatim.

    Matthew 21:5 ____

WALKING IN THE WORD

19. Write some slogans to present Jesus to the world as Savior and Lord.

"Then said Jesus unto them, Be not afraid: go tell my brethren that they go into Galilee, and there shall they see me." (Matthew 28:10, KJV)

APRIL 17, 2022

THE PASCHAL LAMB LIVES!

MATTHEW 28:1–10

Use with Bible Study Guide 7.

WORDS, PHRASES, AND DEFINITIONS

Write the definition of the following words.

1. Paschal lamb: ______
2. Overwhelming: ______
3. Sabbath: ______
4. Sepulchre: ______
5. Countenance: ______
6. Raiment: ______
7. Crucified: ______
8. Hail: ______
9. Censure: ______
10. Grotesque: ______

JUMP-STARTING THE LESSON

11. God answered Sheila and Robert's prayers for a baby when they used what? (In Focus)

    a. ______ Modern medicine

    b. ______ Old-fashioned methods

    c. ______ Patient prayer

12. Name an answer to prayer that you had to wait for a long time. ______

______

______

UNDERSTANDING THE LESSON

13. How is the angel described? (Focal Verses)

a. His face shone like ____________________ (I G L N H T I G N)

b. His clothing was as white as ____________________ (N O S W)

14. How did Jesus treat women? Check all that apply. (The People, Places, and Times)

a. ______ Jesus talked to them.

b. ______ Jesus did not respond to their touch.

c. ______ Jesus healed them.

d. ______ Jesus received their support.

e. ______ Jesus used women as characters in His parables.

15. What part did the women play in the Easter story? (Background)

a. They ran away and hid.

b. They stayed close to the cross.

16. Number each sentence to show the order in which things happened: (In Depth)

______ The women went to visit the tomb.

______ The guards fainted when they saw the angel.

______ There was an earthquake.

______ The angel told the women to tell the disciples.

______ An angel came from heaven and rolled away the stone.

______ The angel told the women that Jesus had been raised from the dead.

______ The women were filled with great joy.

17. To whom did the risen Jesus first appear? ____________________

18. Where would Jesus meet His disciples? ____________________

COMMITTING TO THE WORD

19. Memorize and write verbatim.

Matthew 28:10 ____

____

WALKING IN THE WORD

20. Tell someone this week that Jesus Christ is risen. How might you share that message?

____

____

"If the Son therefore shall make you free, ye shall be free indeed." (John 8:36, KJV)

APRIL 24, 2022

FREEDOM IN CHRIST JESUS

JOHN 8:31–38

Use with Bible Study Guide 8.

WORDS, PHRASES, AND DEFINITIONS

Write the definition of the following words.

1. Bondage: ______________________________
2. Abideth not: ______________________________
3. Abraham's seed: ______________________________
4. Continue in my word: ______________________________
5. Permanent member of the family: ______________________________
6. Providence: ______________________________
7. Abstract theological concepts:______________________________
8. Absolute freedom: ______________________________
9. Academically learned truth: ______________________________
10. Spiritual bondage: ______________________________

JUMP-STARTING THE LESSON

11. What did Earl want to know about his father? Circle all that apply. (In Focus)

    His struggles   His problems   Why he left his family

12. Why did Earl want to see his father? He wanted to find out the __________________ (R U H T T).

UNDERSTANDING THE LESSON

13. Whom did the Jews claim as their most important ancestor? (Focal Verses) ______________________

14. What was the Feast of Tabernacles? Check all that apply. (The People, Places, and Times)

1. ______ It was seven days long.

2. ______ They lived in tabernacles or booths to remind them of their homes in the wilderness.

3. ______ It was the time of the wheat harvest.

4. ______ It was to celebrate God's protection of them.

15. What other ideas are part of the biblical concept of truth? Unscramble the words: (Background)

____________________ (U S I A H F F S N E T L) and ____________________ (T E I I A Y I L L R B)

16. In Christ Jesus lies the ____________________ (W O P R E) to set people ____________________ (R E F E). (In Depth)

17. What were the people blind to? How sin keeps them in spiritual ____________________ (O N B A D G E)

18. When we are freed from sin, what are we free to do? We are free to ____________________ (V E S R E) God instead.

COMMITTING TO THE WORD

19. Memorize and write verbatim.

John 8:36 ____

____

____

____

____

WALKING IN THE WORD

20. Examine your own life for ways in which you are still in bondage to sin. List at least one condition from which you wish to be set free.

____

____

____

____

____

"For if we have been planted together in the likeness of his death, we shall be also in the likeness of his resurrection." (Romans 6:5, KJV)

MAY 1, 2022

FREEDOM FROM SIN

ROMANS 6:1–14

Use with Bible Study Guide 9.

WORDS, PHRASES, AND DEFINITIONS

Write the definition of the following words.

1. Grace: ____________________
2. Discern: ____________________
3. Reflective: ____________________
4. Sever: ____________________
5. Abound: ____________________
6. Henceforth: ____________________
7. Dominion: ____________________
8. Reckon ye: ____________________
9. Reign: ____________________
10. Instrument of evil: ____________________

JUMP-STARTING THE LESSON

11. What assignment was Monica given after she was ordained? (In Focus)

    ____________________ Ministry Leader

12. What was the big change in Monica's life?

    She went from recruiting young girls to be in her ____________________ to winning ____________________ for Jesus.

UNDERSTANDING THE LESSON

13. Unscramble the words: (Focal Verses)

What does going down into the waters of baptism signify?

We are ____________________ (U R B I D E) with Christ.

What does coming up from the waters of baptism signify?

We are ____________________ (A I S R D E) with Christ.

14. Finish the two definitions: (The People, Places, and Times)

Grace: God's ____________________ (N E D U R S E V E D) love and favor toward sinful humans.

Law: God's ____________________ (M E N A C O D N T S M M) given to show us how to live.

15. Who gives the new Christian the new nature? (Background) The Holy ____________________

16. The Holy Spirit sanctifies us by separating us from the ____________________ (O R E P W) of sin and restoring to us a new ____________________ (A U Q T Y I L) of life (In Depth).

17. Since we are crucified with Christ we should count ourselves ____________________ (E A D D) to sin and ____________________ (L V E I A) to God.

18. What should happen in our new life? Sin should not ____________________ (E R I N G) over us, as it did before our salvation.

COMMITTING TO THE WORD

19. Memorize and write verbatim.

Romans 6:5 ____

____

____

WALKING IN THE WORD

20. Paul uses the metaphor of death several ways in this passage. What things does he compare to death, and why are those apt comparisons?

____

____

____

"For I reckon that the sufferings of this present time are not worthy to be compared with the glory which shall be revealed in us." (Romans 8:18, KJV)

MAY 8, 2022

FREEDOM FOR THE FUTURE

ROMANS 8:18–30

Use with Bible Study Guide 10.

WORDS, PHRASES, AND DEFINITIONS

Write the definition of the following words.

1. I reckon: ______________________________
2. Earnest expectation: ______________________________
3. Manifestation: ______________________________
4. Creature: ______________________________
5. Bondage of corruption: ______________________________
6. Groaneth and travaileth: ______________________________
7. Firstfruits of the Spirit: ______________________________
8. To wit: ______________________________
9. Helpeth our infirmities: ______________________________
10. Maketh intercession: ______________________________

JUMP-STARTING THE LESSON

11. What was Thomas's weakness? (In Focus):

    He always arrived for work ____________________.

12. What caused him to try to change his habit?

    He realized his actions had a ____________________ ____________________ on others.

UNDERSTANDING THE LESSON

13. What did God plan for us to be? (Focal Verses):

He predestined us to be __________________ to the __________________ of His Son.

F O C N O M R D E   G A I M E

14. What are four reasons we may suffer? (The People, Places, and Times).

a. The effects of __________________.

b. The consequence of our own __________________.

c. Because we live in a __________________ world.

d. We suffer at the hands of the __________________.

15. What two kinds of people are there? (Background)

Those who live according to the __________________.

Those who live according to the __________________.

16. When will God's glory be revealed in us? (In Depth)

In the age to __________________.

17. Who helps us with the weakness in our praying effectively?

The Holy __________________.

18. Predestination means that God has always known who would be __________________.

COMMITTING TO THE WORD

19. Memorize and write verbatim.

Romans 8:18 ____

____

____

WALKING IN THE WORD

20. Create a song or poem to praise and thank God for the hope He gives in times of trouble.

____

____

____

"And if ye be Christ's, then are ye Abraham's seed, and heirs according to the promise." (Galatians 3:29, KJV)

MAY 15, 2022

FREEDOM AND THE LAW

GALATIANS 3:18–29

Use with Bible Study Guide 11.

WORDS, PHRASES, AND DEFINITIONS

Write the definition of the following words.

1. Abraham's seed: ______________________________
2. Wherefore then serveth: ______________________________
3. The seed: ______________________________
4. Mediator: ______________________________
5. Justified by faith: ______________________________
6. Schoolmaster: ______________________________
7. Under guard: ______________________________
8. Guardian: ______________________________
9. Covenant: ______________________________
10. Benevolent master: ______________________________

JUMP-STARTING THE LESSON

11. What did Hilton have to go through before completing the program to become a teacher? (In Focus)

    Learning as a ____________________ teacher

12. What does "a salary commensurate with other teachers" mean?

    A salary ____________________ (Q E A L U) with other teachers.

UNDERSTANDING THE LESSON

13. The law was given until the seed came. Who was the seed? (Focal Verses) ______________________________

14. What were God's promises to Abraham? Check all that apply. (The People, Places, and Times)

a. ______ God would give him a son.

b. ______ His descendants would become a nation.

c. ______ All nations would be blessed through Jesus, Abraham's descendant.

15. Label each sentence as true or false.

a. ________________ Slaves were a fifth of the Roman population.

b. ________________ Slaves could never be freed.

c. ________________ Slaves were entrusted with the care of children, slave or free.

16. How could Gentiles become Christians? (Background)

a. Gentiles had to become Jews in order to follow Jesus.

b. Gentiles could become Christians by faith alone.

17. What was the purpose of the law? (In Depth)

a. To show us what sin is.

b. To save people through obedience.

18. What happened when Jesus came?

Faith in Jesus makes us the ____________________ (I L H R C D E N) of Abraham.

COMMITTING TO THE WORD

19. Memorize and write verbatim.

Galatians 3:29 ____

____

____

WALKING IN THE WORD

20. We have been freed from slavery to sin. Write down how this has affected your life.

____

____

____

____

"For all the law is fulfilled in one word, even in this; Thou shalt love thy neighbour as thyself." (Galatians 5:14, KJV)

MAY 22, 2022

THE NATURE OF CHRISTIAN FREEDOM

GALATIANS 5:1–15

Use with Bible Study Guide 12.

WORDS, PHRASES, AND DEFINITIONS

Write the definition of the following words.

1. Legalism: ____________________
2. Calculating: ____________________
3. Catering to their fleshly desires: ____________________
4. Yoke of bondage: ____________________
5. Circumcised: ____________________
6. Justified by the law: ____________________
7. Availeth any thing: ____________________
8. Hinder: ____________________
9. None otherwise minded: ____________________
10. Bear his judgment: ____________________

JUMP-STARTING THE LESSON

11. What was Elijah's reason for overworking in good deeds? (In Focus)

    He thought he had to do those things to get to ____________________.

12. What did he not understand? God has freely given us His ____________________.

UNDERSTANDING THE LESSON

13. What is the summary of the law? (Focal Verses)

_____________________ your neighbor as yourself.

14. Where would you find Galatia on a modern map? (The People, Places, and Times)

North central _____________________ (U K T R Y E)

15. Why did the Judaizers say that Gentile Christians had to be circumcised and obey other parts of the Mosaic law? (Background)

To be _____________________ (U S T F J I E D I) with God.

16. What is wrong with following the law? (In Depth)

Keeping the whole law is _____________________ (P O S I M S B L E I).

17. What lie did the false teachers tell about Paul?

They said he had _____________________ (N G A H C D E) his teaching.

18. How should the Galatians use their freedom in Christ?

They should _____________________ (V E S R E) each other in _____________________ (E L V O).

COMMITTING TO THE WORD

19. Memorize and write verbatim.

Galatians 5:14 ____

____

____

____

WALKING IN THE WORD

20. Do something to demonstrate love to someone else, and write down what you did and your motivation.

____

____

____

____

____

“If we live in the Spirit, let us also walk in the Spirit.” (Galatians 5:25, KJV)

MAY 29, 2022

THE SPIRITUAL FRUIT OF FREEDOM

GALATIANS 5:16–26

Use with Bible Study Guide 13.

WORDS, PHRASES, AND DEFINITIONS

Write the definition of the following words.

1. Relational qualities: ______
2. Auxiliaries: ______
3. Discern: ______
4. Lust of the flesh: ______
5. Fornication: ______
6. Lasciviousness: ______
7. Variance: ______
8. Emulations: ______
9. Seditions: ______
10. Temperance: ______

JUMP-STARTING THE LESSON

11. How did Cassandra feel when Lisa got married and moved away? (In Focus) All ______.

12. How did the other women help Cassandra? Circle all that apply.

    a. Stopped by her home.

    b. Prayed for her.

    c. Formed a prayer group which included Cassandra.

UNDERSTANDING THE LESSON

13. Match KJV phrases to NLT phrases that mean the same thing: (Focal Verses)

a. Walk in the Spirit
b. Fruit of the Spirit
c. Lust of the flesh

1. What the Holy Spirit produces
2. Let the Holy Spirit guide you
3. Sinful desires

14. Finish the definitions: (The People, Places, and Times)

Judaizers: Taught that all Christians must follow the ____________________.

Christians: Those who only followed the ____________________.

15. What is the Law lacking in power to obey it? (Background)

The ____________________ (W P R O E) of the ____________________ (L Y O H) Spirit.

16. What is the purpose of the Law? (In Depth)

To shed light on ____________________.

17. Look at the NLT and circle the sins it mentions.

a. Sexual immorality
b. Quarreling
c. Lying
d. Jealousy
e. Outbursts of anger
f. Envy
g. Drunkenness
h. Wild parties

18. Look at the NLT and circle the fruit of the Spirit it mentions:

a. Love
b. Joy
c. Peace
d. Patience
e. Kindness
f. Goodness
g. Humility
h. Faithfulness
i. Gentleness
j. Self-control

COMMITTING TO THE WORD

19. Memorize and write verbatim.

Galatians 5:25 ____

____

____

WALKING IN THE WORD

20. What can you do this week to help someone who is struggling to live a life centered on Jesus Christ?

____

____

____

"Thus shall they be unto thee with whom thou hast laboured, even thy merchants, from thy youth: they shall wander every one to his quarter; none shall save thee." (Isaiah 47:15, KJV)

JUNE 5, 2022

GOD FORETELLS DESTRUCTION

ISAIAH 47:10–15

Use with Bible Study Guide 1.

WORDS, PHRASES, AND DEFINITIONS

Write the definition of the following words.

1. Grapple: ____________________
2. Free ride scholarship: ____________________
3. Ivy League school: ____________________
4. Investment banking: ____________________
5. Flaunt: ____________________
6. With whom thou hast laboured: ____________________
7. Perverted: ____________________
8. Enchantments: ____________________
9. Prognosticators: ____________________
10. Astrologers: ____________________

JUMP-STARTING THE LESSON

11. Circle the things that Jeremy had: (In Focus)

    Scholarship   Big salary   Good job   Close relationship with God   Wife and children

12. What separated Jeremy from God? (R E P I D) ____________________

UNDERSTANDING THE LESSON

13. What were the people trusting in? (Focal Verses)

    (I C K W N S E D E S) ____________________

14. Mark each part of Isaiah's ministry: (The People, Places, and Times)

   a. ______ His ministry is summarized as judgment, renewal, and hope.

   b. ______ He foretold Judah's Babylonian captivity.

   c. ______ Isaiah's prophecies were directed only at Israel.

   d. ______ He foretold the coming of the Messiah.

15. What did God allow when the people of Judah sinned against God?

   The Babylonians took them into ____________________ (X L I E E).

16. Which king did Isaiah say would help restore the Israelites from exile? (Background)

   Nebuchadnezzar   Cyrus   Leonidas

17. God was going to punish Babylon for ____________________ (R D I P E) in their sorcery and supposed ____________________ (N W K O D L E G E). (In Depth)

18. What did Babylon think their astrologers could do? They could ____________________ (T R C O N O L) their ____________________ (T R U F U E).

19. What will break the pride of Babylon? The ____________________ (V R E S O E G N I) will of God.

COMMITTING TO THE WORD

20. Memorize and write verbatim:

   Isaiah 47:15 ____

WALKING IN THE WORD

21. Write a prayer for our nation, specifically for the pride of our country.

> *"Thus saith the LORD, In an acceptable time have I heard thee, and in a day of salvation have I helped thee: and I will preserve thee, and give thee for a covenant of the people, to establish the earth, to cause to inherit the desolate heritages." (Isaiah 49:8, KJV)*

JUNE 12, 2022

GOD FORETELLS REDEMPTION

ISAIAH 49:1–11

Use with Bible Study Guide 2.

WORDS, PHRASES, AND DEFINITIONS

Write the definition of the following words.

1. Desolate heritages: ______________________________
2. Polished shaft: ______________________________
3. Quiver: ______________________________
4. For nought and in vain: ______________________________
5. Abhorreth: ______________________________
6. Sun smite them: ______________________________
7. Redeemer: ______________________________
8. Enigmatic: ______________________________
9. Yahweh: ______________________________
10. Redemptive: ______________________________

JUMP-STARTING THE LESSON

11. What was Harriet Tubman's greatest accomplishment? (In Focus):

    She helped more than 300 slaves escape to ____________________.

12. How can you spread the Word of God to help people come to freedom in Christ? ____________________

    ____

UNDERSTANDING THE LESSON

13. When did God call His servant? Fill in the words for the NLT verses: (Focal Verses)

    The Lord called the Messiah from before ____________________, from within the ____________________.

14. The people of Israel suffered much, especially in exile, but whom did Isaiah prophesy would suffer for the nations? (The People, Places, and Times)

The Suffering Servant who was also God's perfect Servant, ____________________.

15. In the previous chapter, God rebuked the negative attitude of His children. Then He offers

____________________ (O H E P) and ____________________ (P L E H) with the promise of the

____________________'s (E H I S A M S) coming. (Background)

16. God promises the Redeemer will bring: (In Depth)

a. ______ Light

b. ______ Healing

c. ______ Restoration

d. ______ Salvation only to the Jewish people

17. The first Christian missionaries were ____________________ (W I J S H E) people.

18. What does God do for His sheep, according to these verses?

a. ______ He leads the sheep to green pastures.

b. ______ He keeps His sheep away from scorching sun.

c. ______ He guards them from jackals.

d. ______ He leads them to good feeding grounds and fresh water.

COMMITTING TO THE WORD

19. Memorize and write verbatim:

Isaiah 49:8 ____

____

____

WALKING IN THE WORD

20. Whom can you tell this week about God's never-ending love and salvation for all people?

____

____

____

"And kings shall be thy nursing fathers, and their queens thy nursing mothers: they shall bow down to thee with their face toward the earth, and lick up the dust of thy feet; and thou shalt know that I am the LORD: for they shall not be ashamed that wait for me." (Isaiah 49:23, KJV)

JUNE 19, 2022

GOD'S RESTORED PEOPLE SHALL PROSPER

ISAIAH 49:18–23

Use with Bible Study Guide 3.

WORDS, PHRASES, AND DEFINITIONS

Write the definition of the following words.

1. Restoration: ____________________
2. Accountant: ____________________
3. Recipient: ____________________
4. Indescribable faithfulness: ____________________
5. Nursing fathers: ____________________
6. Lick up the dust of thy feet: ____________________
7. Desolate places: ____________________
8. Too strait: ____________________
9. Begotten: ____________________
10. Set up my standard: ____________________

JUMP-STARTING THE LESSON

11. What was Jakiesha upset about? (In Focus)

    She liked things done a ____________________ (T N E R C I A) way.

12. She needed to ____________________ (P A L O G O E Z I) to Pastor Fred and the congregation.

UNDERSTANDING THE LESSON

13. Unscramble the encouraging words in Isaiah 49:18, NLT: (Focal Verses)

    All your ______________ (H D C I R L N E) will come ______________ (A K C B) to you.

14. What is the "Progeny Blessing?" Fill in the blanks with the words below: (The People, Places, and Times)

Having ________________ as ________________ to continue the ________________ people of God.

COVENANT HEIRS CHILDREN

15. Why were God's people in captivity? (Background)

They were ________________ (S T B O T E N A I) and ________________ (B U T B S N R O).

16. Isaiah's words, spoken during the exile, are intended to ________________ (C E U N G A O R E) God's people. (In Depth)

17. What does the widowed mother suddenly see? She is surrounded with more children than she ________________ (wants/lost).

18. Which does Isaiah prophesy that the godless people will do for God's people?

a. ______ They will carry your little sons back in their arms.

b. ______ They will bring your daughters on their shoulders.

c. ______ They will serve you and care for all your needs.

COMMITTING TO THE WORD

19. Memorize and write verbatim:

Isaiah 49:23 ____

____

____

____

____

WALKING IN THE WORD

20. Write down something you need to do to restore a relationship with a family member or friend.

____

____

____

____

____

"Hearken to me, ye that follow after righteousness, ye that seek the LORD: look unto the rock whence ye are hewn, and to the hole of the pit whence ye are digged." (Isaiah 51:1, KJV)

JUNE 26, 2022

GOD OFFERS DELIVERANCE

ISAIAH 51:1–8

Use with Bible Study Guide 4.

WORDS, PHRASES, AND DEFINITIONS

Write the definition of the following words.

1. Speak disparagingly: ______________________________
2. Bondage: ______________________________
3. Sovereign Lord: ______________________________
4. Vindicates me: ______________________________
5. Advocate: ______________________________
6. Hearken: ______________________________
7. Sarah that bare you: ______________________________
8. Isles: ______________________________
9. Wax old like a garment: ______________________________
10. Reproach: ______________________________

JUMP-STARTING THE LESSON

11. Why was Kaylynn in prison? (In Focus)

    For a ____________________ he did not ____________________.

12. What did Kaylynn advocate for?

    He fought for the ____________________ of all people

UNDERSTANDING THE LESSON

13. To whom is the passage directed? (Focal Verses)

    All who ____________________ the ____________________.

14. Which are true about Abraham and Sarah? (The People, Places, and Times)

a. ______ They were not perfect.

b. ______ They were wealthy merchants.

c. ______ They grew closer to God with time.

d. ______ God was working out His plans for them.

15. What were missing from the Garden of Eden?

____________________ (E W D E S) and ____________________ (O N H T R S)

16. What did God call out three times? (Background)

He called people to ________________________ (I S N L T E) to His plan for

________________________ (L V E A N D E C E I R)

17. Match the sentences to show how God will comfort His people: (In Depth)

a. God will restore Zion	1. From despair.
b. God will give them	2. Hearts that are glad.
c. They will be	3. Songs of joy
d. They will sing	4. Thankful to God

18. Who will receive God's fulfilled promises?

God's ____________________ (O P E L P E) will see the fulfillment of those promises.

19. Fill in the two sentences with the right words: criticism, salvation

a. God's ____________________ and righteousness will always exist.

b. Do not fear the ____________________ of people.

COMMITTING TO THE WORD

20. Memorize and write verbatim:

Isaiah 51:1 ____

____

WALKING IN THE WORD

21. What is an area in your life where you need to demonstrate your faith in God more?

____

____

"All things were made by him; and without him was not any thing made that was made."
(John 1:3, KJV)

JULY 3, 2022

THE CREATING WORD BECOMES FLESH

JOHN 1:1–14

Use with Bible Study Guide 5.

WORDS, PHRASES, AND DEFINITIONS

Write the definition of the following words.

1. Dwelt: ______________________________
2. Existed: ______________________________
3. Extinguish: ______________________________
4. The will of the flesh: ______________________________
5. Gnosticism: ______________________________
6. Intimately familiar: ______________________________
7. Thriving: ______________________________
8. Amid: ______________________________
9. Heresy: ______________________________
10. In tandem with: ______________________________

JUMP-STARTING THE LESSON

11. Circle the things that were formerly true of Sister Nancy: (In Focus)

    Alcoholic   Abused her husband   Sold drugs   Abused her children

12. How did Nancy turn herself around?

    She gave her ____________________ (F E L I) to ____________________ (H C S T I R).

UNDERSTANDING THE LESSON

13. Which are true of Jesus? (Focal Verses)

a. ______ Is a god

b. ______ Is the Word

c. ______ Was with God in the beginning

d. ______ Is God

14. John's purpose in his Gospel was to explain Christian ________________________ (O H T E O G Y L). (The People, Places, and Times)

15. Why do scholars think that the apostle John is the author of the Gospel of John? (Background)

a. ______ He was the disciple that Jesus loved.

b. ______ He wrote to discourage Jewish believers in Jesus.

c. ______ He was eyewitness to many of the events in the Gospel of John.

d. ______ He was the youngest disciple.

16. Jesus is the Word, *logos* in the Greek language. (In Depth)

a. The Greeks understood *logos* to mean the thought or ____________________ in the mind.

b. The Jews understood *logos* to mean the personification of ____________________.

17. What was the message of John the Baptist?

Jesus is the ____________________ (H L I G T) of the world.

18. What right comes to those who believe on Jesus and receive Him.

The right to become His ____________________ (L I H C R N E D).

COMMITTING TO THE WORD

19. Memorize and write verbatim.

John 1:3 ____

____

WALKING IN THE WORD

20. Find someone this week with whom you can share the true identity of Jesus and how to have a relationship with Him. What will you say to this person?

____

____

JULY 10, 2022

"So the father knew that it was at the same hour, in the which Jesus said unto him, Thy son liveth: and himself believed, and his whole house." (John 4:53, KJV)

THE WORD HEALS

JOHN 4:46–54

Use with Bible Study Guide 6.

WORDS, PHRASES, AND DEFINITIONS

Write the definition of the following words.

1. Besought: ______________________
2. Ere: ______________________
3. Began to amend: ______________________
4. Palsy: ______________________
5. Compelled: ______________________
6. Hindered: ______________________
7. Manifestation: ______________________
8. Unrestrained: ______________________
9. Relegated: ______________________
10. Dismantled: ______________________

JUMP-STARTING THE LESSON

11. Circle Thomas's problems that God through HOPE church helped him with: (In Focus)

    Partial blindness   no food for his daughters   death of his wife

12. The congregation, pastor, and Thomas all ______________ because God had performed a ______________!

UNDERSTANDING THE LESSON

13. What had previously happened in Cana of Galilee? (Focal Verses)

    a. Jesus made water into wine.

    b. Jesus was baptized.

    c. A nobleman/government official came to see Jesus.

14. Which are true about Capernaum? (The People, Places, and Times)

a. ______ It was a central location of Jesus' earthly ministry.

b. ______ Peter's home there became the residence for Jesus.

c. ______ Jesus was baptized here by John the Baptist.

15. What happened in Samaria? (Background)

a. The Samaritan woman was the first person to whom Jesus revealed His identity.

b. The Samaritan woman told all her neighbors about Jesus.

c. Jesus asked the Samaritan woman for a drink of water.

16. Which were the flawed beliefs of the nobleman? (In Depth)

a. He needed to walk 16 miles to talk to Jesus.

b. Jesus could heal his son.

c. Jesus could only heal his son if He were physically present.

17. Which did Jesus challenge the nobleman to believe?

a. ______ Jesus was interested in this healing because this was a nobleman.

b. ______ Jesus is the Messiah.

c. ______ His word is as powerful as His presence when believed.

18. God's power is unhindered by ____________________ (M E T I) and ____________________ (P C A S E).

19. The nobleman learned the correlation between ____________________ (I A H T F) and ____________________ (I C L E S M A R).

COMMITTING TO THE WORD

20. Memorize and write verbatim.

John 4:53 ______________________________

____

____

WALKING IN THE WORD

21. Many situations require us to have faith in more than just for physical healing. Ask God for healing in one area of your life today.

____

____

> *"Jesus said unto her, I am the resurrection, and the life: he that believeth in me, though he were dead, yet shall he live: And whosoever liveth and believeth in me shall never die. Believest thou this?" (John 11:25–26, KJV)*

JULY 17, 2022

THE WORD RESURRECTS THE DEAD

JOHN 11:17–27, 38–44

Use with Bible Study Guide 7.

WORDS, PHRASES, AND DEFINITIONS

Write the definition of the following words.

1. Engage with: ____________________
2. Nigh: ____________________
3. Fifteen furlongs: ____________________
4. If thou hadst: ____________________
5. Resurrection: ____________________
6. Thou hearest me: ____________________
7. Graveclothes: ____________________
8. Bound about: ____________________
9. Napkin: ____________________
10. Loose him: ____________________

JUMP-STARTING THE LESSON

11. Why was Franklin in a church again? (In Focus) ____________________
12. What kind of hope was Franklin thinking about?

    The hope of ____________ ____________ through Jesus Christ.

UNDERSTANDING THE LESSON

13. How long had Lazarus been in the grave when Jesus arrived? (Focal Verses) ____________ days
14. Underline the things we have learned about Martha (The People, Places, and Times)

    a. She was the older sister of Mary and Lazarus.

b. She was the owner of the house.

c. She wanted to listen to Jesus while Mary served the dinner.

15. Write true or false by things we learn about Bethany:

a. ________________ Bethany is a village on the eastern slope of the Mount of Olives.

b. ________________ Jesus liked to stay there when He came to Jerusalem.

c. ________________ He was in the home of Peter the Leper when He was anointed days before His death.

16. Put the story in numerical order: (Background)

a. ______ Mary and Martha notify Jesus that Lazarus is very sick.

b. ______ By the time Jesus arrives, Lazarus has been dead four days.

c. ______ Jesus stays where He is for two more days.

17. Jesus' delay was for the __________________ of His disciples, Mary, and Martha. (In Depth)

18. What was Martha not expecting? An __________________ miracle.

19. What did Jesus say? "I am the resurrection and the __________________."

20. What did Jesus need to do to raise Lazarus from the dead?

a. ______ Pray loudly.

b. ______ Simply speak the command.

c. ______ Lay hands on Lazarus.

COMMITTING TO THE WORD

21. Memorize and write verbatim.

John 11:25–26 ____

____

____

WALKING IN THE WORD

22. In what ways is the funeral of a Christian different from those of others?

____

____

____

JULY 24, 2022

"I am come a light into the world, that whosoever believeth on me should not abide in darkness." (John 12:46, KJV)

THE WORD SAVES

JOHN 12:44–50

Use with Bible Study Guide 8.

WORDS, PHRASES, AND DEFINITIONS

Write the definition of the following words.

1. Abide: ______________________________
2. Trinity: ______________________________
3. Hosanna: ______________________________
4. Pharisees: ______________________________
5. Parable: ______________________________
6. Laments: ______________________________
7. Persisted in unbelief: ______________________________
8. Mourns: ______________________________
9. Redemption: ______________________________
10. Farewell address: ______________________________

JUMP-STARTING THE LESSON

11. What was Dr. Garrett's frequent prayer? (In Focus)

    "God, let Your ____________________ be done in my life."

12. What did God call Dr. Garrett to do?

    Go to ____________________ as a ____________________ team member.

UNDERSTANDING THE LESSON

13. Jesus declared: "I am the ____________________ of the world." (Focal Verses)

14. Name the three Persons of the Trinity: (The People, Places, and Times)

    ____________________, ____________________, and ____________________.

15. Jesus lamented over the ____________________ of the land. (Background)

16. Which things caused Jesus to mourn? (In Depth)

    a. ______ The people did not believe that God sent Him.

    b. ______ The people were blind to who Jesus was.

    c. ______ The people did not like His miracles.

17. What happens to people who put their trust in Jesus?

    They will no longer remain in ____________________ (K N E S D R A S).

18. How can people avoid the penalty of death? They can ____________________ (C E P A C T) Jesus.

19. Every word that Jesus spoke came directly from God the ____________________ (H T F A R E).

COMMITTING TO THE WORD

20. Memorize and write verbatim.

    John 12:46 ____

WALKING IN THE WORD

21. Share with someone this week the benefits of eternal life in Jesus Christ.

"And I will pray the Father, and he shall give you another Comforter, that he may abide with you for ever." (John 14:16, KJV)

JULY 31, 2022

THE WORD GIVES PEACE

JOHN 14:15-29

Use with Bible Study Guide 9.

WORDS, PHRASES, AND DEFINITIONS

Write the definition of the following words.

1. Prince of darkness: ____________________
2. Comforter: ____________________
3. Advocate: ____________________
4. Abide: ____________________
5. Dwell: ____________________
6. Manifest: ____________________
7. Abode: ____________________
8. Perspective: ____________________
9. Extortionists: ____________________
10. Messianic claims: ____________________

JUMP-STARTING THE LESSON

11. Which did James do when he and his wife experienced tension in their marriage? (In Focus)

    a. ______ He asked his wife if everything was all right.

    b. ______ He bought flowers and chocolates for his wife.

    c. ______ He asked the Holy Spirit to show him what to do.

12. What did the Holy Spirit show him to do?

    a. ______ Tell his wife how much he still appreciated her and loved her.

    b. ______ Make a big romantic gesture.

UNDERSTANDING THE LESSON

13. Match words from the KJV to current usage: (Focal Verses)

a. Seeth	1. Keeps
b. Knoweth	2. Sees
c. Keepeth	3. Knows
d. Saith	4. Says

14. Circle names for the Holy Spirit: (The People, Places, and Times)

Holy Ghost   Spirit of God   Spirit of Christ   Spirit of Truth   Comforter   Counselor

15. Match the phrase to the end of the sentence: (Background)

a. The disciples were scared because	1. The Jewish establishment.
b. Jesus was on a collision course with	2. They would be alone in a hostile world.
c. The disciples did not understand	3. Many of the things Jesus said and did.

16. What did Jesus say the Holy Spirit would reveal to His followers? (In Depth)

He would reveal the ____________________ about Jesus.

17. What will those who love Jesus do? They will ____________________ His words.

18. What would be the two functions of the Holy Spirit for the disciples?

a. He would ____________________ (M E R D I N) them of the teaching of Jesus.

b. He would help them ____________________ (N R U D S N T A E D) the ministry of Jesus.

COMMITTING TO THE WORD

19. Memorize and write verbatim.

John 14:16 ____

____

____

WALKING IN THE WORD

20. Look around your community and find out where the Holy Spirit is at work empowering people to do the work of Jesus. Ask the Holy Spirit how you can help.

____

____

> *"And God shall wipe away all tears from their eyes; and there shall be no more death, neither sorrow, nor crying, neither shall there be any more pain: for the former things are passed away." (Revelation 21:4, KJV)*

AUGUST 7, 2022

A NEW HOME

REVELATION 21:1–8

Use with Bible Study Guide 10.

WORDS, PHRASES, AND DEFINITIONS

Write the definition of the following words.

1. Unique genre: ____________________
2. Apocalypse: ____________________
3. The tabernacle of God: ____________________
4. Alpha: ____________________
5. Omega: ____________________
6. Abominable: ____________________
7. Whoremongers: ____________________
8. Sorcerers: ____________________
9. Brimstone: ____________________
10. Martyred: ____________________

JUMP-STARTING THE LESSON

11. Randy wished he had a ____________ (C N D E S O) ____________ (N A H C E C). (In Focus)
12. What did someone share with him for a new beginning? The ____________ (O S P L G E)

UNDERSTANDING THE LESSON

13. What did John see in his vision? (Focal Verses)

    A new ____________ and a new ____________.

14. Which are true about John? (The People, Places, and Times)

    a. ______ He witnessed the Transfiguration.

b. ______ He was told to care for the mother of Jesus.

c. ______ He was martyred like all the other disciples.

d. ______ He wrote the Gospel of John, three epistles, and Revelation.

e. ______ He was the father of Zebedee and the son of James.

15. What does Revelation say about the Bride of Christ?

a. ______ She is the church, those who have a relationship with Christ.

b. ______ She is also called the Bride of the Lamb.

c. ______ Christ is the Bridegroom.

d. ______ She becomes the bride because of her righteous deeds.

e. ______ She becomes the bride through God's saving grace.

16. Order John's four visions in Revelation: (Background)

a. ______ Christ on Mount Zion

b. ______ Jesus and His messages to the seven churches

c. ______ The fulfillment of God's promise in Christ.

d. ______ Jesus at the throne of God opening the seven seals

17. Where do we find the account of the creation of the world? (In Depth) ____________________.

What does God create in Revelation 21:1-2? ____________________.

18. Where did God fellowship with Adam and Eve? ____________________.

Where will God come to dwell with His people? ____________________.

19. What is the first death? Physical death on ____________________ (E R H T A).

What is the second death? ____________________ (N E R A L T E) separation from God.

COMMITTING TO THE WORD

20. Memorize and write verbatim.

Revelation 21:4 ____

____

WALKING IN THE WORD

21. Name one of God's promises that you especially appreciate. How can you share that with others this week?

____

____

"And the wall of the city had twelve foundations, and in them the names of the twelve apostles of the Lamb." (Revelation 21:14, KJV)

AUGUST 14, 2022

A NEW CITY

REVELATION 21:9–21

Use with Bible Study Guide 11.

WORDS, PHRASES, AND DEFINITIONS

Write the definition of the following words.

1. Foundation: ________________________________
2. Apostles: ________________________________
3. The Lamb: ________________________________
4. Vials: ________________________________
5. Come hither: ________________________________
6. Descending: ________________________________
7. Jasper stone: ________________________________
8. Reed: ________________________________
9. Foursquare: ________________________________
10. Furlongs: ________________________________

JUMP-STARTING THE LESSON

11. What had Katheryn's new husband chosen for her? (In Focus) A new ____________________.

12. What do Barry's preparations show Katheryn?

    His love for her   His desire to make her happy   His sense for interior design

UNDERSTANDING THE LESSON

13. Put the right number in front of each, either 7 or 12. (Focal Verses)

    a. ______ Foundations

    b. ______ Angels

c. ______ Vials

d. ______ Gates total

e. ______ Apostles

f. ______ Tribes

g. ______ Last plagues

14. Which describe the New Jerusalem? (The People, Places, and Times)

a. ______ It will be built by God.

b. ______ It is a symbol of hope only for the Jewish nation.

c. ______ The righteous will live in it in perfect peace forever.

d. ______ It is a symbol of the church as the redeemed Bride of Christ.

15. What is the believer's inheritance? (Background)

Being with ____________________ Himself in all His ____________________!

16. If the church is the bride of Christ, what does it tell us about Jesus, the bridegroom? (In Depth)

Jesus sealed His covenant of marriage with His very own ____________________.

17. What are the 12 foundations named after? The twelve ____________________.

18. What do the 12 stones adorning the walls remind the Jews of? The high priest's ____________________.

COMMITTING TO THE WORD

19. Memorize and write verbatim.

Revelation 21:14 ____

____

____

WALKING IN THE WORD

20. How do you feel about waiting for the new city?

____

____

____

"And he shewed me a pure sign of water of life, clear as crystal, proceeding out of the throne of God and of the Lamb." (Revelation 22:1, KJV)

AUGUST 21, 2022

THE RIVER OF LIFE

REVELATION 22:1–7

Use with Bible Study Guide 12.

WORDS, PHRASES, AND DEFINITIONS

Write the definition of the following words.

1. Biblical references: ____________________
2. Material effect: ____________________
3. Spiritual effect: ____________________
4. Symbolic effect: ____________________
5. Tangible reminder: ____________________
6. Redemptive plan: ____________________
7. Proceeding out of: ____________________
8. Bare: ____________________
9. Sovereignty: ____________________
10. Vicarious suffering: ____________________

JUMP-STARTING THE LESSON

11. What was 95-year-old Cattie looking forward to right now? (In Focus)

    The arrival of her first two ____________-____________-____________.

12. What was she thinking a lot about now? ____________

UNDERSTANDING THE LESSON

13. Where is the water of life coming from? (Focal Verses)

    From the ____________ (H R N T E O) of God.

14. What idea is seen in calling Christ the Lamb? (The People, Places, and Times)

a. ______ Christ was slain for our redemption from sin.

b. ______ Christ was a springtime baby.

15. Which are true for both Christ's first coming and His second coming? (Background)

a. ______ Fulfillment of the prophecies

b. ______ Great news for some

c. ______ Bad news for others

d. ______ He begins as a baby

16. Which will be in the future home for Christians? (In Depth)

a. ______ Fifteen kinds of fruit

b. ______ River with the water of life

c. ______ Tree of life

17. Write true or false in front of each thing that occurs because of the presence of God.

a. ________________ The curse has been canceled.

b. ________________ Christians cannot look upon the face of God.

c. ________________ God's name will be written on their hands.

18. Why do we know these prophecies are true?

a. ______ God inspires the prophets.

b. ______ The visions John has seen are inspired by God.

c. ______ Jesus says He is coming soon.

COMMITTING TO THE WORD

19. Memorize and write verbatim.

Revelation 22:1 ____

____

WALKING IN THE WORD

20. Write down some ways in which you will be obedient to the Lord in order to be ready for His return.

____

____

____

> *"For I testify unto every man that heareth the words of the prophecy of this book, If any man shall add unto these things, God shall add unto him the plagues that are written in this book: And if any man shall take away from the words of the book of this prophecy, God shall take away his part out of the book of life, and out of the holy city, and from the things which are written in this book."*
> *(Revelation 22:18–19, KJV)*

AUGUST 28, 2022

COME AND ENJOY

REVELATION 22:10–21

Use with Bible Study Guide 13.

WORDS, PHRASES, AND DEFINITIONS

Write the definition of the following words.

1. Seal not: ______________________________
2. Dogs: ______________________________
3. Maketh a lie: ______________________________
4. Root of David: ______________________________
5. Offspring of David: ______________________________
6. Vile: ______________________________
7. Messianic longing: ______________________________
8. Alpha: ______________________________
9. Omega: ______________________________
10. Woeful news: ______________________________

JUMP-STARTING THE LESSON

11. Why did Jason read the last chapter of the Bible first? (In Focus)

    He wanted to see how ____________________ was going to come out.

12. What did Jason discover by reading the last chapter of the Bible first?

    Christians are assured of the ultimate ____________________ ending.

UNDERSTANDING THE LESSON

13. What can Christians say as we wait? (Focal Verses): ____________________, Lord Jesus.

14. What is Jesus saying about Himself as He says He is the Alpha and Omega? (The People, Places, and Times)

  a. ______ He is the source of everything.

  b. ______ He is the Beginning and the End.

  c. ______ He reigns over every aspect of His creation.

15. Revelation is both a book of ____________________ (R O I P S M E) and a book of ____________________ (N W R A N G I). (Background)

16. Who guides John through his vision? (In Depth) An ____________________.

17. Which does Jesus say?

  a. ______ I am coming.

  b. ______ I am the Aleph and the Tau.

  c. ______ I will bring rewards.

  d. ______ I am the Root and Offspring of David.

18. Who invites people to come?

  a. ______ The Holy Spirit

  b. ______ The bride (Christians)

  c. ______ Christ

  d. ______ John

COMMITTING TO THE WORD

19. Memorize and write verbatim.

Revelation 22:18–19 ____

____

____

____

WALKING IN THE WORD

20. Look over today's Scripture passage and write down the things you find most surprising.

____

____

____

____

ANSWER KEY

SEPTEMBER–NOVEMBER 2021

ANSWER KEY TO LESSON 1 – SEPTEMBER 5, 2021

1. Redeemed: Purchased
2. Habitation: Home
3. Anguish: Sorrow
4. Sanctuary: A holy place
5. Timbrel: Tambourine
6. Genocide: Killing a whole people based upon their race or ethnic identity
7. Annihilation: Complete destruction
8. Inhabitants: People living in the land
9. Surpassed: Better than
10. Holiness: Perfection
11. SAFETY
12. Praise; good
13. a. sea, b. waters
14. a. false, b. true, c. true, d. true
15. a. 2, b. 1, c. 4, d. 3
16. PRAISE
17. HEARD
18. REMEMBER
19. "Who is like unto thee, O LORD, among the gods? who is like thee, glorious in holiness, fearful in praises, doing wonders?"
20. Answers will vary.

ANSWER KEY TO LESSON 2 – SEPTEMBER 12, 2021

1. Cherubim: Angels of a specific order
2. Psaltery: Ancient stringed instrument
3. Lyre: A stringed instrument, similar to a harp
4. Cornet: A brass-wind instrument, similar to a trumpet
5. Castanet: An instrument consisting of two spoon-shaped shells tapped together
6. Ephod: A priestly garment made of fine linen
7. Tabernacle: A place of worship composed of a wooden structure covered with curtains
8. Flagon: A measure of wine or a pressed cake of raisins
9. Extraction: Something taken out
10. Deterred: Prevented
11. STYLE
12. PRAYED
13. KJV: 1. Harps, 2. Psalteries, 3. Timbrels, 4. Cornets, 5. Cymbals; NLT: 1. Lyres, 2. Harps, 3. Tambourines, 4. Castanets, 5. Cymbals
14. 3., 1., 4., 2., 5.
15. The relocation of the Ark
16. Upon a new cart
17. On the shoulders of the Levite priests
18. 2., 3., 1., 4.
19. "And David and all the house of Israel played before the LORD on all manner of instruments made of fir wood, even on harps, and on psalteries, and on timbrels, and on cornets, and on cymbals."
20. Answers will vary.

ANSWER KEY TO LESSON 3 – SEPTEMBER 19, 2021

1. Mercy: Help that is not necessarily deserved
2. Jewish heritage: Jewish by ancestry
3. Royal lineage: Descended from King David
4. Metaphor: A picture to give greater understanding
5. Exercise his faith: Demonstrate his trust in Jesus
6. Hindrance: Something that gets in the way
7. Religious obligation: Just something that one feels one

ought to do

8. Marginalized by society: Ignored by most people
9. Narrative: Story
10. Impending: Happening soon
11. Tornado
12. Guitar, chair
13. Nazareth, Jericho, Bartimaeus
14. Joshua and his forces destroyed the city; Zacchaeus lived in the city.
15. Bartimaeus to Rabboni and Son of David; The crowd to Jesus of Nazareth
16. David, mercy
17. The crowd, Bartimaeus, Jesus, the crowd
18. See
19. "And Jesus answered and said unto him, What wilt thou that I should do unto thee? The blind man said unto him, Lord, that I might receive my sight.
20. Answers will vary.

ANSWER KEY TO LESSON 4 – SEPTEMBER 26, 2021

1. Monsoons: Heavy, seasonal rains
2. Doctrine: Basic teaching
3. Exalted: Raised up to a place of great honor
4. Untoward: Sinful, crooked
5. Apostles: The original disciples who were present during the life of Jesus on earth
6. Had all things common: Shared everything they had
7. One accord: Together, in agreement
8. Firstfruits: The first and best of the farmer's crops
9. Bestowal: Give, confer
10. Convicting: Feeling sorry for one's sins
11. Soup, beds
12. Walls, church
13. Raised
14. Feast, Weeks
15. The Holy Spirit
16. The Father → the Son → the Holy Spirit
17. BORN-AGAIN BELIEVER
18. Underline all four.
19. "And they continued stedfastly in the apostles' doctrine and fellowship, and in breaking of bread, and in prayers."
20. Answers will vary.

ANSWER KEY TO LESSON 5 – OCTOBER 3, 2021

1. Endureth: Lasts, continues
2. Commodity: Farm product to be sold
3. Analogy: A picture of, a resemblance between two things
4. Zion: God's name for the city of Jerusalem
5. Pilgrimage: March toward Jerusalem for a special time of worship
6. Enthrone Him: Formally crown Him as King
7. Gates: The entrance to the city of Jerusalem
8. Liturgical psalm: Scripture passage recited as a call to worship
9. Summons: Invitation, a special call
10. Exhortation: Encouragement to do, not a command
11. CHOREOGRAPHY, POSITIONING
12. SINGING, CHEERING
13. 1.—b., 2.—e., 3.—f., 4.—c., 5.—d., 6.—a.
14. Care
15. They were the people of God united by their worship of the one true God.
16. All people
17. Circle all the words.
18. Check all the words.
19. "Know ye that the LORD he is God: it is he that hath made us, and not we ourselves; we are his people, and the sheep of his pasture."
20. Answers will vary.

ANSWER KEY TO LESSON 6 – OCTOBER 10, 2021

1. Complacent: Lazy and uninterested
2. Convened: Met
3. Cronies: Partners in poor government
4. Galvanized: Urged to action
5. Satest: Fully satisfied

6. Inquisition: Formal court hearing
7. Parallelism: Thoughts running side by side
8. Superscription: Note written outside
9. Corporate: As a group
10. Laud: Praise
11. Run against them
12. Change
13. OPPRESSED, HELPLESS, HUMBLE
14. 73, 12, 10, 2, 1, 1, 1
15. Power, justice
16. Right, fairness
17. RIGHT, JUST
18. "And he shall judge the world in righteousness, he shall minister judgment to the people in uprightness."
19. Answers will vary.

ANSWER KEY TO LESSON 7 – OCTOBER 17, 2021

1. Cardiac arrest: The heart stops completely or has a dangerous rhythm
2. Arterial blockage: The arteries become blocked due to fatty deposits on the inner walls
3. Stent: A tube inserted in an artery to open it up
4. Minished: Decreased, diminished
5. Whoso: Whoever
6. Levites: Descendants of the tribe of Levi who had special religious service, but were not priests
7. Onerous: Burdensome, oppressive
8. Admonishing: Warning, reproving, exhorting
9. Exile: Forced removal from one's land
10. Dispersed: Separated into different areas
11. Circle everything but pain in the heart.
12. Stent
13. REDEEMED
14. 1400 BC, 400 BC
15. Exile
16. Good, love
17. Cried
18. Faithful love
19. "Then they cried unto the LORD in their trouble, and he delivered them out of their distresses."
20. Answers will vary.

ANSWER KEY TO LESSON 8 – OCTOBER 24, 2021

1. Amiable: Beautiful, delightful
2. Selah: Musical term meaning to pause; interlude
3. Lord of hosts: God, the Commander of all the armies of angels
4. Remnant: Those who are left
5. Insatiable: Incapable of ever having enough
6. Catalyst: Something that brings about a reaction
7. Edifices: Buildings
8. Blessed: Happy
9. Meditate: Think upon
10. Anointed: One set aside as a prophet, priest, or king
11. Circle all but Europe.
12. Family home in South Carolina
13. What joy
14. b. and c.
15. Underline all three.
16. a., b., c.
17. strength
18. Hear my prayer.
19. Thousand
20. "Blessed are they that dwell in thy house: they will be still praising thee. Selah."
21. Answers will vary.

ANSWER KEY TO LESSON 9 – OCTOBER 31, 2021

1. Meek: Humble
2. Firmament: Heaven
3. Hallelujah: Praise the Lord
4. Embodied: Made concrete, put in bodily form
5. Feat: Act
6. Vindicate: To avenge, justify, defend
7. Vast expanse: Very large area

8. Repertoire: A list of music and types of music one is prepared to perform
9. Admonition: A command
10. Dominant message: Main idea
11. Classical, Negro spirituals
12. Scholarship
13. Check all three
14. a. to 2., b. to 4., c. to 1., d. to 3., e. to 5.
15. HALLELUJAH PSALMS
16. New
17. CARING FOR HIS PEOPLE
18. Both
19. "Let every thing that hath breath praise the LORD. Praise ye the LORD."
20. Answers will vary.

ANSWER KEY TO LESSON 10 – NOVEMBER 7, 2021

1. Tribulation: A time of extreme suffering and persecution
2. Kindred: Persons related to each other
3. Arrayed: Clothed
4. Exiled: Forcibly removed from one's country, forced to a different particular area
5. Scroll: Rolled up style of book
6. Interlude: Lull, intermission
7. Redeemed: Purchased by the blood of Jesus, saved by the blood of Jesus
8. Mandated: Necessitated
9. Garments: Clothing
10. Tabernacle: God's Temple as a tent
11. All of these.
12. Praise God for being with her.
13. a. and c.
14. a. and d.
15. Both of these
16. Interlude
17. Underline all three.
18. Circle all seven.
19. Overcome
20. "And I said unto him, Sir, thou knowest. And he said to me, These are they which came out of great tribulation, and have washed their robes, and made them white in the blood of the Lamb."
21. Answers will vary.

ANSWER KEY TO LESSON 11 – NOVEMBER 14, 2021

1. Sovereignty: Supreme power over all
2. Subsidiaries: Companies owned and directed by another company
3. Reign: Rule as king
4. Elicit fear: To drum up fear
5. Unadulterated: Not watered down
6. Unhindered: Not ceasing, not stopping
7. Heralding: Proclaiming
8. Consecrated purpose: Dedicated purpose
9. Endeavoring: Trying to
10. Contemporary terrestrial church: The modern church on the Earth
11. ADDING RESOURCES
12. WORK-LIFE
13. For ever and ever
14. Circle all five.
15. WORSHIP
16. a., b., d., e.
17. Lightning, Thunder, Earthquakes, Voices, Great hail
18. "And the seventh angel sounded; and there were great voices in heaven, saying, The kingdoms of this world are become the kingdoms of our Lord, and of his Christ; and he shall reign for ever and ever."
19. Answers will vary.

ANSWER KEY TO LESSON 12 – NOVEMBER 21, 2021

1. Implications: Unsaid truths
2. Propagate: Spread, multiply
3. Whore: Prostitute
4. Fornication: Immorality, sex outside of marriage, adultery

5. Avenge: Giving a deserved punishment
6. Omnipotent: All powerful, all mighty
7. Arrayed: Dressed up
8. Imagery: Word pictures
9. Emblematic: Symbolic
10. Marginalized: Outside of being accepted
11. CRIMES, COMMITTED
12. Justice, served
13. MARRIAGE, LAMB
14. a. to 2., b. to 3., c. to 1.
15. Babylon
16. Babylon, judged/punished
17. Paid, sin, Cross
18. "Let us be glad and rejoice, and give honour to him: for the marriage of the Lamb is come, and his wife hath made herself ready."
19. Answers will vary.

ANSWER KEY TO LESSON 13 – NOVEMBER 28, 2021

1. Portrayal: Portrait, picture
2. Deity: God
3. Graven image: Idol
4. Quick and dead: The living and the dead
5. Tongues: Languages
6. Magnify: Give glory to, praise
7. Gentile: Anyone who is not Jewish
8. Adhered: Stuck, clung, believed
9. Centurion: Roman army captain over a large number of soldiers
10. Piety: Godliness
11. Brown-skinned Jewish Israeli
12. DIVIDE, CONFUSION
13. Peace
14. a., b., and c.
15. 1, 4, 2, 3.
16. SALVATION, BELIEVE
17. GOOD NEWS, LIFE, WATER, HOLY SPIRIT
18. "Then Peter opened his mouth, and said, Of a truth I perceive that God is no respecter of persons: But in every nation he that feareth him, and worketh righteousness, is accepted with him."
19. Answers will vary.

DECEMBER 2021-FEBRUARY 2022

ANSWER KEY TO LESSON 1 – DECEMBER 5, 2021

1. Statutes: Permanent laws
2. Covenant: Solemn agreement
3. Plaister: Plaster
4. Burnt offerings: A perfect male animal sacrifice that was completely burned up
5. Peace offerings: The organs of a male or female that was burned up
6. Hearken: Listen
7. Decrees: Decisions given by God
8. Threshold: Sill or plank that lies under the door
9. Heirs: Those who inherit upon the death of a relative
10. Prohibitions: Things forbidden
11. Equal
12. Law
13. FEAR, WALK, LOVE, SERVE
14. It was meant to show one's complete devotion to God.
15. a. five—ten, b. Dead—Red, c. Twelve—Ten, d. Babylon—heaven, e. waterfall—rock
16. loving, just
17. "And now, Israel, what doth the LORD thy God require of thee, but to fear the LORD thy God, to walk in all his ways, and to love him, and to serve the LORD thy God with all thy heart and with all thy soul, To keep the commandments of the LORD, and his statutes, which I command thee this day for thy good?"
18. Answers will vary.

ANSWER KEY TO LESSON 2 – DECEMBER 12, 2021

1. Equity: Equality, fairness in dealing
2. High stakes: High risk, dangerous

3. Deployment: Movement of troops, bringing on additional troops
4. Shew: Show
5. Art thou: Are you
6. Fetched: Went and got
7. Alway: Always
8. Summoned: Called
9. Lame: Crippled
10. Abnormality: Out of the usual
11. Look, each other
12. Adopt
13. MEPHIBOSHETH
14. a., b.
15. a. enemies, friends; b. David, Jonathan; c. Forgot, remembered
16. just, kind
17. Angry
18. All of these
19. "And David said, Is there yet any that is left of the house of Saul, that I may shew him kindness for Jonathan's sake?
20. Answers will vary.

ANSWER KEY TO LESSON 3 – DECEMBER 19, 2021

1. Commodity: Valuable thing
2. Stablish: Establish
3. Divide the spoil: Divide the plunder, divide up the valuables taken in battle
4. Yoke of his burden: Chains that tie up his people
5. Staff: Whip or a stick used for support
6. Rod of his oppressor: Weapon of his enemy
7. Garments rolled in blood: Clothing stained with blood
8. Turbulent: full of conflict and disorder
9. Vassal state: State that is obligated to another
10. Tribute: Payment made as a sign of dependence
11. Excited, peace, quiet
12. Tranquility, peace
13. WONDERFUL COUNSELLOR, MIGHTY GOD, EVERLASTING FATHER, PRINCE PEACE
14. b., c., d.
15. faithful
16. sin, Jesus Christ
17. Davidic; bring, rule
18. "Of the increase of his government and peace there shall be no end, upon the throne of David, and upon his kingdom, to order it, and to establish it with judgment and with justice from henceforth even for ever. The zeal of the LORD of hosts will perform this."
19. Answers will vary.

ANSWER KEY TO LESSON 4 – DECEMBER 26, 2021

1. Inclusion: Included within a group
2. Marginalized: Treated as outside the accepted group
3. Vulnerable: Susceptible to harm, needing special care
4. Frankincense: Sap or resin from a tree in Africa or the Middle East that smells fragrant, especially when burned
5. Myrrh: Sap or resin used in creating fragrant oil
6. Privily: Privately
7. Diligently: Working hard with great care
8. Magi: Member of Persian priestly caste, or sorcerer
9. Tremendous architectural feats: Amazing buildings
10. Paranoia: Unwarranted feelings that others are persecuting you or intend to harm you
11. HOMELESS IMMIGRANT
12. IMMIGRATION
13. Governor, Ruler
14. a., b., c.
15. a., d.
16. David
17. Bethlehem
18. ANOTHER
19. "And when they were come into the house, they saw the young child with Mary his mother, and fell down, and worshipped him: and when they had opened their treasures, they presented unto him gifts; gold, and frankincense and myrrh."
20. Answers will vary.

ANSWER KEY TO LESSON 5 – JANUARY 2, 2022

1. Bear the brunt: Experience the pain
2. Deluged: Flooded
3. God's grace sustained: God helped with troubles
4. Tiller of the ground: Farmer
5. Firstlings of the flock: Firstborn and best of the sheep
6. Wroth: Angry
7. Fugitive: One running from punishment
8. Vagabond: Homeless wanderer
9. Slay: Kill
10. Vengeance: Punishment
11. temper
12. a. anger, b. Christ
13. Sin
14. a. Firstborn, b. Firstfruits
15. a. Abel, b. Cain
16. God
17. "Am I my brother's keeper?"
18. REPENT, RECONCILE
19. "And he said, What hast thou done? the voice of thy brother's blood crieth unto me from the ground."
20. Answers will vary.

ANSWER KEY TO LESSON 6 – JANUARY 9, 2022

1. Aileth: Troubles
2. Descendants: Heirs
3. Weaned: Stopped breast-feeding
4. Cast: Throw out, get rid of
5. Bondwoman: Slave, servant
6. Hearken: Listen
7. Bow shot: About 100 yards, as far as when a bow is shot
8. Archer: One who makes his living by shooting animals with a bow and arrow
9. Hostility: Unfriendliness, opposition
10. Turmoil: Confusion, disturbance
11. a., b.
12. College, honors
13. With
14. b., c., d.
15. b., c.
16. Isaac
17. Bless
18. Cry
19. a., b., c., d.
20. "And God heard the voice of the lad; and the angel of God called to Hagar out of heaven, and said unto her, What aileth thee, Hagar? fear not; for God hath heard the voice of the lad where he is. Arise, lift up the lad, and hold him in thine hand; for I will make him a great nation.
21. Answers will vary.

ANSWER KEY TO LESSON 7 – JANUARY 16, 2022

1. Renegotiate: Bargain again to get a difference in the agreement
2. Impartial: Not showing favorites
3. Wrest judgment: Twist justice
4. Put not thine hand with the wicked: Do not cooperate with evil people
5. Take no gift: Take no bribe
6. Do not oppress a stranger: Do not hurt a foreigner
7. Sow thy land: Plant and harvest your land
8. Son of thy handmaid: Son of your slaves
9. Covenant: Formal agreement to do what is specified
10. Imperative: Command
11. safe, welcoming
12. lease, landlord
13. a., b.
14. GOSSIP, SLANDER
15. The Ten Commandments
16. a., c., d., e., g.
17. friend, foe
18. blind
19. a., b., c.
20. "Thou shalt not follow a multitude to do evil; neither shalt thou speak in a cause to decline after many to wrest judgment: Neither shalt thou countenance a poor man in his cause."

21. Answers will vary.

ANSWER KEY TO LESSON 8 – JANUARY 23, 2022

1. Entailed: Included as a necessary part
2. Collaborative environment: An environment where the input of everyone is encouraged
3. Galvanize: Stimulate
4. Integrity: Morally upright, sound, honest
5. Invested: Contributed time, money, and emotional attachment
6. Aligned with his values: Shared the same moral principles
7. Wrest judgment: Twist justice or judgment
8. Verdict: Decision in a court case
9. Purge the evil: Get rid of sinful behavior
10. Cumbersome: Clumsy, troubling
11. together
12. Christ
13. a. to 3, b. to 1, c. to 2.
14. a. Tabernacle; b. Jerusalem.
15. example, power, blessing, justice
16. priests
17. "Judges and officers shalt thou make thee in all thy gates, which the LORD thy God giveth thee, throughout thy tribes. and they shall judge the people with just judgment."
18. Answers will vary.

ANSWER KEY TO LESSON 9 – JANUARY 30, 2022

1. Disenfranchised: Someone deprived of the vote
2. Fetch his pledge: Take back the item given in security
3. Raiment: Cloak, coat
4. Bondman: Slave
5. Redeemed thee from thence: Paid the price to save one from slavery
6. Sheaf: Bundle of grain
7. Beatest thine olive tree: Shake the olive tree so the ripe olives fall off
8. Glean: Going back a second time to pick up the harvest missed on the first pass
9. Destitute laborers: Workers not making enough to live on
10. Absolved: Exempted from or not required to do
11. Laid off
12. a., c., d.
13. Stranger, fatherless, and widow or foreigner, orphan, and widow
14. a., b., c.
15. dignity
16. a. Willingness, b. Fidelity
17. Retaliatory violence
18. Needy
19. "But thou shalt remember that thou wast a bondman in Egypt, and the LORD thy God redeemed thee thence: therefore I command thee to do this thing."
20. Answers will vary.

ANSWER KEY TO LESSON 10 – FEBRUARY 6, 2022

1. Ewe lamb: Female lamb
2. Bosom: Chest
3. Dressed: Prepared for serving to eat
4. Kindled: Stoked like a hot fire
5. Fourfold: Four times over
6. Howbeit: Nevertheless, however
7. Ironically: Opposite of what would be expected
8. Not exempt from the consequences: Will have to bear the consequences, even though forgiven
9. God's omniscient view: God's almighty ability to see and know everything
10. Curry favor: Trying to do whatever it takes to win the favor of the king or other people in high places
11. a., b.
12. consequences
13. SHEEP, LAMB
14. a. and d. to Nathan; b. and c. to David
15. A. SHEPHERD, B. PLUCK
16. a.
17. a. repentance, b. guilt
18. sinned, Lord

19. "And Nathan said to David, Thou art the man."
20. Answers will vary.

ANSWER KEY TO LESSON 11 – FEBRUARY 13, 2022

1. Insurmountable: Problems that cannot be overcome
2. Statutes: Written laws
3. Judgments: Legal decisions
4. Decrees: Official orders
5. Scribe in the law of Moses: Lawyer who specialized in the interpretation of the Law
6. Granted: Officially gave
7. Priests: Those in charge of administering worship in the Temple
8. Levites: Singers
9. Porters: Gatekeepers
10. Nethinims: Temple servers
11. hurricane, everything
12. a. faith, community; b. prayer, thanksgiving
13. on or upon
14. Cyrus, Darius, Xerxes, Artaxerxes
15. 1, 3, 2, 4.
16. All three
17. a., c.
18. All of these
19. "For Ezra had prepared his heart to seek the law of the LORD, and to do it, and to teach in Israel statutes and judgments."
20. Answers will vary.

ANSWER KEY TO LESSON 12 – FEBRUARY 20, 2021

1. Grated on him: Bothered him
2. Pervert justice: Twist justice
3. Transgression: Sin
4. Betimes: Early, before the expected or usual time
5. Supplication to the Almighty: Pray to God
6. Make the habitation of thy righteousness prosperous: Make your home successful
7. Though thy beginning was small: Though you began with poverty
8. Thy latter end should greatly increase: You will end up rich
9. Dwelling place of the wicked shall come to nought: The house of the wicked will come to nothing
10. Theodicy: Study of why God allows bad things to come to good people
11. thanked
12. do this
13. justice
14. Cross out a., b., c.
15. Check a., b.
16. a. just, b. punish, c. obedient, d. repentant
17. "Then answered Bildad the Shuhite, and said, How long wilt thou speak these things? and how long shall the words of thy mouth be like a strong wind?"
18. Answers will vary.

ANSWER KEY TO LESSON 13 – FEBRUARY 27, 2022

1. Hideth counsel: Question God's wisdom
2. Abhor: Hate
3. Turned the captivity: Restored the fortunes
4. Fair: Lovely
5. Oddly archaic: Strangely old-fashioned
6. Prologue: A separate, introductory section
7. Epilogue: A separate section, a conclusion
8. Appease God: To satisfy the wrath of God
9. Preempts: Takes action to prevent something from happening
10. Nuanced: Subtle characteristics
11. drugs
12. Pastor, church
13. eyes
14. 2. Poetry, 3. Epilogue, 1. Prologue
15. pain, righteous
16. EVERYTHING
17. PERSONAL, PERCEPTION
18. FORTUNES
19. ADVERSITY

20. "Who is he that hideth counsel without knowledge? therefore have I uttered that I understood not; things too wonderful for me, which I knew not."
21. Answers will vary.

MARCH-MAY 2022

ANSWER KEY TO LESSON 1 - MARCH 6, 2022

1. Feasible: Possible to do
2. Proclamation: Official announcement
3. He hath charged me: He has appointed me
4. Sojourneth: Lives in a foreign land
5. Beasts: Livestock
6. Freewill offering: Voluntary offering
7. Captives: Those taken by force
8. Asses: Donkeys
9. Threescore: Sixty
10. Dram: Small piece of money
11. Crumbling, shifting, cracking, small
12. Pray
13. Jeremiah
14. a., b.
15. a., c.
16. SHEER REBELLION
17. a. Cyrus; b. God appointed him to rebuild the temple; c. Hearts willing to answer God's call; d. Construction of the temple
18. "And some of the chief of the fathers, when they came to the house of the LORD which is at Jerusalem, offered freely for the house of God to set it up in his place."
19. Answers will vary.

ANSWER KEY TO LESSON 2 - MARCH 13, 2022

1. Pivotal: Very important
2. Postpartum: After giving birth to a baby
3. Alter: Change
4. Decree: Law
5. Violates: Crosses a line; fails to obey
6. Diligence: Speed, studiousness
7. Rolls: Records, archives
8. Bullocks: Bulls
9. Savours: Pleasant smell
10. Dunghill: Garbage dump
11. Praying, celebrating, and comforting
12. DOCTOR
13. a. builded, b. king's house, c. restored
14. a. Tatnai or Tattenai b. Darius
15. a., b., d.
16. a., b.
17. governor, officials
18. a. sacrifices, b. executed
19. "And the God that hath caused his name to dwell there destroy all kings and people, that shall put to their hand to alter and to destroy this house of God which is at Jerusalem. I Darius have made a decree; let it be done with speed."
20. Answers will vary.

ANSWER KEY TO LESSON 3 - MARCH 20, 2022

1. Prevailed: Won the victory
2. Rams: Adult male sheep
3. Unintentional sins: Sins not done on purpose
4. Bronze laver: Wash basin for the priests
5. Molten sea: Large basin in the Temple to hold water
6. Trans-Euphrates: Land to the west of the Euphrates River
7. Reinstituting: Introducing again
8. Divine intervention: Involvement of God in human affairs
9. Unleavened bread: Bread made without yeast
10. Procrastinate: Put off doing something
11. Circle everything but "Finding a famous architect."
12. EVERYONE REJOICED
13. Circle Tatnai and Shetharboznai
14. a. to 2.; b. to 3.; c. to 1.
15. a. Cyrus, b. Darius
16. dedicated, joy
17. sacrifice, sins
18. Passover, Bread
19. "And the children of Israel, the priests, and the

Levites, and the rest of the children of the captivity, kept the dedication of this house of God with joy."

20. Answers will vary.

ANSWER KEY TO LESSON 4 – MARCH 27, 2022

1. Humility: Modest view of one's own importance
2. Beware: Watch out!
3. Sware: Swore, promised
4. Raiment: Clothing
5. Waxed not old: Did not get old
6. Proceedeth out of the mouth: Words that came out of the mouth
7. Chasteneth his son: Scolded or punished his son
8. Scarceness: Not very much
9. Sustain: Support
10. Polarized politics: Political views or parties that cause people to go to one extreme or the other
11. CUT, ADVICE
12. THANK YOU
13. Check all except the last
14. COMPLAINED
15. GENERATION
16. Ten
17. a. to 3, b. to 2, c. to 1.
18. Circle all.
19. "Beware that thou forget not the LORD thy God, in not keeping his commandments, and his judgments, and his statutes, which I command thee this day."
20. Answers will vary.

ANSWER KEY TO LESSON 5 – APRIL 3, 2022

1. Perspective: Point of view
2. Unleavened bread: Bread made with no yeast
3. Passover: Special dinner to remember that God saved the Israelites and brought them to freedom from slavery
4. Remission of sins: Cancelation of debt owed due to sin
5. Testament: Formal agreement, covenant
6. Covenant: Formal agreement, testament
7. Mark my words: Remember what I said
8. Messianic title: Title of the anointed Savior
9. The elect: People chosen by God to be saved
10. Provisional victory: Hypothesizing a win until the complete victory comes
11. UNBEARABLE
12. LIFE, CHRIST
13. a. to 1, b. to 3, c. to 2, d. to 7, e. to 6, f. to 8, g. to 5, h. to 4.
14. a., b., c.
15. a., b., c., d.
16. LIBERATION, OPPRESSION
17. 2, 1, 3, 6, 4, 5
18. "But I say unto you, I will not drink henceforth of this fruit of the vine, until that day when I drink it new with you in my Father's kingdom."
19. Answers will vary.

ANSWER KEY TO LESSON 6 – APRIL 10, 2022

1. Nomad: One who wanders without a permanent home
2. Triumphal Entry: Entering a city with a large parade celebrating victory
3. Drew nigh: Approached, got close
4. Any man say ought: Any man says anything
5. Daughter of Sion: Daughter of Zion, Jewish people, Jerusalem
6. Foal of an ass: Donkey's colt
7. Strawed them: Spread them
8. Hosanna: "Lord, save us," a shout of praise
9. Procession: Informal parade
10. Replete: complete, filled out
11. a., b.
12. a., c.
13. King
14. King, Priest
15. a., b., c.
16. HUMILITY
17. PROPHET
18. "Tell ye the daughter of Sion, Behold, thy King cometh unto thee, meek, and sitting upon an ass, and a colt the foal of an ass."
19. Answers will vary.

ANSWER KEY TO LESSON 7 – APRIL 17, 2022

1. Paschal lamb: Passover lamb
2. Overwhelming: Very great in amount
3. Sabbath: Jewish day of worship, Saturday
4. Sepulchre: Tomb
5. Countenance: Face
6. Raiment: Clothing
7. Crucified: Hung on the cross until dead
8. Hail: Greetings!
9. Censure: Expression of extreme disapproval
10. Grotesque: Distorted, repulsively ugly
11. c.
12. Answers will vary.
13. a. LIGHTNING, b. SNOW
14. a., c., d., e.
15. b.
16. 1, 4, 2, 6, 3, 5, 7
17. The women
18. Galilee
19. "Then said Jesus unto them, Be not afraid: go tell my brethren that they go into Galilee, and there shall they see me."
20. Answers will vary.

ANSWER KEY TO LESSON 8 – APRIL 24, 2022

1. Bondage: Slavery
2. Abideth not: Does not live there permanently
3. Abraham's seed: Abraham's descendants
4. Continue in my word: Keep on obeying God's commandments
5. Permanent member of the family: Actual family member
6. Providence: God's spiritual care for His children
7. Abstract theological concepts: Deep thoughts difficult to understand
8. Absolute freedom: Not slaves to sin
9. Academically learned truth: Understood only in the mind
10. Spiritual bondage: Slavery to sin
11. Circle all three.
12. TRUTH
13. Abraham
14. 1, 2, 4.
15. FAITHFULNESS, RELIABILITY
16. POWER, FREE
17. BONDAGE
18. SERVE
19. "If the Son therefore shall make you free, ye shall be free indeed."
20. Answers will vary.

ANSWER KEY TO LESSON 9 – MAY 1, 2022

1. Grace: Unearned favor from God
2. Discern: Understand
3. Reflective: Thinking about
4. Sever: Cut off
5. Abound: Exist in large numbers
6. Henceforth: From now on
7. Dominion: Rule over, boss
8. Reckon ye: Consider yourself
9. Reign: Control
10. Instrument of evil: Tools for doing sin
11. Baptism
12. gang, souls
13. BURIED, RAISED
14. UNDESERVED, COMMANDMENTS
15. Spirit
16. POWER, QUALITY
17. DEAD, ALIVE
18. REIGN
19. "For if we have been planted together in the likeness of his death, we shall be also in the likeness of his resurrection."
20. Answers will vary.

ANSWER KEY TO LESSON 10 – MAY 8, 2022

1. I reckon: I think
2. Earnest expectation: Waiting eagerly
3. Manifestation: That which is revealed or shown
4. Creature: Anything created by God
5. Bondage of corruption: Slavery to sin
6. Groaneth and travaileth: Groans and works hard

7. Firstfruits of the Spirit: Just a taste of what the Holy Spirit has for us
8. To wit: That is
9. Helpeth our infirmities: Helps us with our weaknesses
10. Maketh intercession: Prays for
11. late
12. negative impact
13. CONFORMED, IMAGE
14. a. sin, b. actions, c. sinful, d. devil
15. Flesh, Spirit
16. come
17. Spirit
18. His
19. “For I reckon that the sufferings of this present time are not worthy to be compared with the glory which shall be revealed in us.”
20. Answers will vary.

ANSWER KEY TO LESSON 11 – MAY 15, 2022

1. Abraham’s seed: Abraham’s children, his descendants
2. Wherefore then serveth: What was the purpose
3. The seed: Jesus, the descendant of Abraham
4. Mediator: Peace-maker between two parties
5. Justified by faith: Made right with God by faith in Jesus Christ
6. Schoolmaster: Teacher, guardian
7. Under guard: Being watched or one’s protection
8. Guardian: Teacher, guard
9. Covenant: Sworn agreement, oath
10. Benevolent master: Kind slave master
11. student
12. EQUAL
13. Jesus
14. a., b., c.
15. a. True, b. False, c. True
16. b.
17. a.
18. CHILDREN
19. “And if ye be Christ’s, then are ye Abraham’s seed, and heirs according to the promise.”
20. Answers will vary.

ANSWER KEY TO LESSON 12 – MAY 22, 2022

1. Legalism: Depending on moral law rather than faith in Jesus Christ
2. Calculating: Acting in a scheming way
3. Catering to their fleshly desires: Giving in to sinful behavior
4. Yoke of bondage: Slavery to sin
5. Circumcised: Having removed the foreskin, which the Jews did to show their covenant with God
6. Justified by the law: Saved through obedience to God’s commandments
7. Availeth any thing: Accomplishes anything
8. Hinder: Stop
9. None otherwise minded: No one who thinks differently
10. Bear his judgment: Suffer God’s punishment
11. Heaven
12. Grace
13. Love
14. TURKEY
15. JUSTIFIED
16. IMPOSSIBLE
17. CHANGED
18. SERVE, LOVE
19. “For all the law is fulfilled in one word, even in this; Thou shalt love thy neighbour as thyself.”
20. Answers will vary.

ANSWER KEY TO LESSON 13 – MAY 29, 2022

1. Relational qualities: Interactions with others
2. Auxiliaries: Support or additional help ministries
3. Discern: Distinguish, recognize, perceive
4. Lust of the flesh: Sinful desires
5. Fornication: Sex outside of marriage
6. Lasciviousness: Sinful sexual desire
7. Variance: Quarreling
8. Emulations: Desires to be better than others
9. Seditions: Fighting against the governments
10. Temperance: Self-control, abstinence from extremes
11. alone
12. a., b., c.
13. a. to 2., b. to 1., c. to 3.

14. Law, Way
15. POWER, HOLY
16. sin
17. All of them except c.
18. All of them except g.
19. "If we live in the Spirit, let us also walk in the Spirit."
20. Answers will vary.

JUNE-AUGUST 2022

ANSWER KEY TO LESSON 1 – JUNE 5, 2022

1. Grapple: Think about and argue with oneself
2. Free ride scholarship: Scholarship that pays for everything
3. Ivy League school: University that is considered one of the best
4. Investment banking: Advisors for corporations and those with much wealth
5. Flaunt: Show off
6. With whom thou hast laboured: People you have worked with
7. Perverted: Twisted, sinful
8. Enchantments: Magic charms
9. Prognosticators: Those who think they can foretell the future
10. Astrologers: Those who think they can tell the future by following the stars
11. Everything but a close relationship with God
12. PRIDE
13. WICKEDNESS
14. a., b., d.
15. EXILE
16. Cyrus
17. PRIDE, KNOWLEDGE
18. CONTROL, FUTURE
19. SOVEREIGN
20. "Thus shall they be unto thee with whom thou hast laboured, even thy merchants, from thy youth: they shall wander every one to his quarter; none shall save thee."
21. Answers will vary.

ANSWER KEY TO LESSON 2 – JUNE 12, 2022

1. Desolate heritages: Inherited land which is now useless
2. Polished shaft: Sharp arrow
3. Quiver: The case for carrying arrows
4. For nought and in vain: For nothing and useless
5. Abhorreth: Hates, detests
6. Sun smite them: Burning sun hurts them
7. Redeemer: One who buys freedom for the slave
8. Enigmatic: Mysterious
9. Yahweh: Name of God meaning His eternal existence
10. Redemptive: Power to save from sin
11. Freedom
12. Answers will vary.
13. Birth, womb
14. Jesus
15. HOPE, HELP, MESSIAH
16. a., b., c.
17. JEWISH
18. a., b., d.
19. "Thus saith the LORD, In an acceptable time have I heard thee, and in a day of salvation have I helped thee: and I will preserve thee, and give thee for a covenant of the people, to establish the earth, to cause to inherit the desolate heritages."
20. Answers will vary.

ANSWER KEY TO LESSON 3 – JUNE 19, 2022

1. Restoration: Returning to the former condition
2. Accountant: Professional who keeps and inspects financial accounts
3. Recipient: One who receives a gift
4. Indescribable faithfulness: Faithfulness too wonderful to describe
5. Nursing fathers: Fathers who care for the needs of the children
6. Lick up the dust of thy feet: So humble they would lick the dust off the feet of others
7. Desolate places: Abandoned land
8. Too strait: Too small
9. Begotten: Natural-born children, not adopted

10. Set up my standard: Lift up my flag
11. CERTAIN
12. APOLOGIZE
13. CHILDREN, BACK
14. CHILDREN, HEIRS, COVENANT
15. OBSTINATE, STUBBORN
16. ENCOURAGE
17. Lost
18. a., b., c.
19. "And kings shall be thy nursing fathers, and their queens thy nursing mothers: they shall bow down to thee with their face toward the earth, and lick up the dust of thy feet; and thou shalt know that I am the LORD: for they shall not be ashamed that wait for me."
20. Answers will vary.

ANSWER KEY TO LESSON 4 – JUNE 26, 2022

1. Speak disparagingly: Say disrespectful things about someone
2. Bondage: Slavery or incarceration
3. Sovereign Lord: God who directs everything
4. Vindicates me: Clears me of blame
5. Advocate: Someone who supports a cause
6. Hearken: Listen
7. Sarah that bare you: Sarah as the ancestor
8. Isles: Islands
9. Wax old like a garment: Wear out like old clothes
10. Reproach: To express disapproval or disappointment
11. Crime, commit
12. Rights
13. Seek, Lord
14. a., c., d.
15. WEEDS, THORNS
16. LISTEN, DELIVERANCE
17. A. to 1., b. to 2., c. to 4., d. to 3.
18. PEOPLE
19. A. salvation, B. criticism
20. "Hearken to me, ye that follow after righteousness, ye that seek the LORD: look unto the rock whence ye are hewn, and to the hole of the pit whence ye are digged."
21. Answers will vary.

ANSWER KEY TO LESSON 5 – JULY 3, 2022

1. Dwelt: Lived
2. Existed: Reality or being
3. Extinguish: Put out
4. The will of the flesh: Human decisions
5. Gnosticism: The belief that matter is evil and that Jesus did come as a real human being
6. Intimately familiar: Knowing someone closely
7. Thriving: Living in health and strength
8. Amid: In the middle of
9. Heresy: False belief
10. In tandem with: Along with
11. Alcoholic, Abused her husband, Abused her children
12. LIFE, CHRIST
13. b., c., d.
14. THEOLOGY
15. a., c., d.
16. Reasoning, Wisdom
17. LIGHT
18. CHILDREN
19. "All things were made by him; and without him was not any thing made that was made."
20. Answers will vary.

ANSWER KEY TO LESSON 6 – JULY 10, 2022

1. Besought: Begged
2. Ere: Before
3. Began to amend: Began to get better
4. Palsy: Paralysis with tremors
5. Compelled: Forced
6. Hindered: Stopped
7. Manifestation: A clear demonstration
8. Unrestrained: Nothing to stop it
9. Relegated: Dismissed to something inferior
10. Dismantled: Took apart
11. Partial blindness, no food for his daughters
12. Rejoiced, miracle

13. a., c.
14. a., b.
15. a., b., c.
16. a., c.
17. b., c.
18. TIME, SPACE
19. FAITH, MIRACLES
20. "So the father knew that it was at the same hour, in the which Jesus said unto him, Thy son liveth: and himself believed, and his whole house."
21. Answers will vary.

ANSWER KEY TO LESSON 7 – JULY 17, 2022

1. Engage with: Become involved with
2. Nigh: Near
3. Fifteen furlongs: About 1.7 miles
4. If thou hadst: If you had
5. Resurrection: Coming back to life after death
6. Thou hearest me: You hear me
7. Graveclothes: Fabric wound around a body in which it is buried
8. Bound about: Wrapped around
9. Napkin: Headcloth
10. Loose him: Unwrap him
11. To attend his friend DeShawn's funeral
12. Eternal life
13. Four
14. a., b.
15. a. true, b. true, c. false
16. a. 1, b. 3., c. 2
17. Benefit
18. Immediate
19. Life
20. b.
21. "Jesus said unto her, I am the resurrection, and the life: he that believeth in me, though he were dead, yet shall he live: And whosoever liveth and believeth in me shall never die. Believest thou this?"
22. Answers will vary.

ANSWER KEY TO LESSON 8 – JULY 24, 2022

1. Abide: Continue living in the Lord
2. Trinity: Three unified as one
3. Hosanna: Save
4. Pharisees: Jewish sect that believed in extreme obedience to the smallest law, but often found ways around it
5. Parable: A simple story to illustrate a spiritual meaning
6. Laments: Expressions of sorrow
7. Persisted in unbelief: Continued not believing in Jesus
8. Mourns: Feels deep sorrow
9. Redemption: The act of being saved
10. Farewell address: Speech given just before leaving a post or job
11. Will
12. Uganda, missionary
13. Light
14. Father, Son, Holy Spirit
15. Unbelief
16. a., b.
17. DARKNESS
18. ACCEPT
19. FATHER
20. "I am come a light into the world, that whosoever believeth on me should not abide in darkness."
21. Answers will vary.

ANSWER KEY TO LESSON 9 – JULY 31, 2022

1. Prince of darkness: The devil
2. Comforter: Holy Spirit
3. Advocate: Holy Spirit
4. Abide: Live
5. Dwell: Live
6. Manifest: Demonstrate
7. Abode: Home
8. Perspective: Opinion
9. Extortionists: People who try to do things through force
10. Messianic claims: Claims that Jesus is the Savior

11. a., c.
12. a.
13. a. to 2., b. to 3., c. to 1., d. to 4.
14. Circle all.
15. a. to 2., b. to 1., c. to 3.
16. Truth
17. Obey
18. REMIND, UNDERSTAND
19. "And I will pray the Father, and he shall give you another Comforter, that he may abide with you for ever."
20. Answers will vary.

ANSWER KEY TO LESSON 10 – AUGUST 7, 2022

1. Unique genre: One-of-a-kind or different style, form, or content
2. Apocalypse: The complete and final destruction of the world
3. The tabernacle of God: The home of God
4. Alpha: The first letter of the Greek alphabet
5. Omega: The last letter of the Greek alphabet
6. Abominable: Corrupt, detestable, horrible
7. Whoremongers: Fornicators, adulterers
8. Sorcerers: People who claim to have magic or occult power
9. Brimstone: Burning sulfur
10. Martyred: Killed for one's beliefs
11. SECOND CHANCE
12. GOSPEL
13. Heaven, earth
14. a., b., d.
15. a., b., c., e.
16. a. 3, b. 1, c. 4, d. 2
17. Genesis 1, A new heaven and new earth
18. The Garden of Eden, the new city/Jerusalem
19. EARTH, ETERNAL
20. "And God shall wipe away all tears from their eyes; and there shall be no more death, neither sorrow, nor crying, neither shall there be any more pain: for the former things are passed away."
21. Answers will vary.

ANSWER KEY TO LESSON 11 – AUGUST 14, 2022

1. Foundation: Base of the building
2. Apostles: Those sent personally by Jesus to evangelize
3. The Lamb: Jesus Christ who gave His life for us
4. Vials: Bottles to hold liquids
5. Come hither: Come here
6. Descending: Coming down
7. Jasper stone: A precious gem, usually green
8. Reed: A hollow stick cut from a water plant
9. Foursquare: All four sides the same length
10. Furlong: About one-eighth of a mile
11. Home
12. His love for her, his desire to make her happy
13. A. 12, b. 7, 12, c. 7, d. 12, e. 12, f. 12, g. 7.
14. a., c., d.
15. God, glory
16. Blood
17. Apostles
18. Breastplate
19. "And the wall of the city had twelve foundations, and in them the names of the twelve apostles of the Lamb."
20. Answers will vary.

ANSWER KEY TO LESSON 12 – AUGUST 21, 2022

1. Biblical references: Bible verses
2. Material effect: A change on material things
3. Spiritual effect: A change that relates to the spirit
4. Symbolic effect: A metaphorical change, rather than a literal one
5. Tangible reminder: Reminder that can be seen
6. Redemptive plan: Plan to save
7. Proceeding out of: Coming out of
8. Bare: Born of
9. Sovereignty: Supreme power and authority
10. Vicarious suffering: Suffering in the place of and for the benefit of others
11. Great, great, grandsons

12. Heaven
13. THRONE
14. a.
15. a., b., c.
16. b., c.
17. a. True, b. False, c. False
18. a., b., c.
19. "And he shewed me a pure sign of water of life, clear as crystal, proceeding out of the throne of God and of the Lamb."
20. Answers will vary.

ANSWER KEY TO LESSON 13 – AUGUST 28, 2022

1. Seal not: Do not lock up
2. Dogs: Hateful people
3. Maketh a lie: Lives a lie
4. Root of David: Creator and source of David
5. Offspring of David: Descended from David
6. Vile: Disgusting
7. Messianic longing: Great desire for the Savior
8. Alpha: First letter of the Greek alphabet
9. Omega: Last letter of the Greek alphabet
10. Woeful news: Very sad, awful news
11. Everything
12. Happy
13. Come
14. a., b., c.
15. PROMISE, WARNING
16. Angel
17. a., c., d.
18. All four
19. "For I testify unto every man that heareth the words of the prophecy of this book, If any man shall add unto these things, God shall add unto him the plagues that are written in this book: And if any man shall take away from the words of the book of this prophecy, God shall take away his part out of the book of life, and out of the holy city, and from the things which are written in this book."
20. Answers will vary.

NOTES

NOTES